FUNDAMENTALS OF ULTRASONICS

ENGLAND:	BUTTERWORTH & CO. (PUBLISHERS) LTD. LONDON: 88 Kingsway, W.C.2
AFRICA:	BUTTERWORTH & CO. (AFRICA) LTD. DURBAN: 33/35 Beach Grove
AUSTRALIA:	BUTTERWORTH & CO. (AUSTRALIA) LTD. SYDNEY: 6/8 O'Connell Street MELBOURNE: 473 Bourke Street BRISBANE: 240 Queen Street
CANADA:	BUTTERWORTH & CO. (CANADA) LTD. TORONTO: 1367 Danforth Avenue, 6
NEW ZEALAND:	BUTTERWORTH & CO. (NEW ZEALAND) LTD. WELLINGTON: 49/51 Ballance Street AUCKLAND: 35 High Street
U.S.A.:	BUTTERWORTH INC. WASHINGTON, D.C.: 7235 Wisconsin Avenue, 14

FUNDAMENTALS
OF
ULTRASONICS

J. BLITZ, M.Sc., A.Inst.P.

Lecturer in Physics,
Brunel College,
London

LONDON
BUTTERWORTHS
1963

Suggested U.D.C. number: 534·321·9

Printed in Great Britain by
The Camelot Press Ltd., London and Southampton

CONTENTS

		Page
FOREWORD	.. ..	ix
1. INTRODUCTION	.. ..	1

2. GENERAL PRINCIPLES OF THE PROPAGATION OF LOW AMPLITUDE WAVES

2.1	General Considerations	5
2.2	Free and Forced Vibrations	5
2.3	Wave Vectors	10
2.4	The Equation of Motion for Plane Waves ..	10
2.5	The Velocity of Plane Waves	11
2.6	Specific Acoustic Impedance	13
2.7	Relationships between the Wave Vectors of Plane Waves	14
2.8	Acoustic Intensity	15
2.9	Pressure of Radiation	16
2.10	Attenuation of Plane Waves	17
2.11	Reflection and Refraction of Plane Waves ..	24
2.12	Diffraction	35
2.13	Acoustic Waveguides	37
2.14	Focussing Systems	37
2.15	The Doppler Effect	38

3. ULTRASONIC GENERATORS AND RECEIVERS

3.1	Introduction	40
3.2	Crystal Oscillators	41
3.3	Piezoelectric Relations	45
3.4	Dynamic Characteristics of Piezoelectric Transducers	50
3.5	Properties of Piezoelectric Crystals	55
3.6	The Preparation and Mounting of Crystal Sources	57
3.7	Crystal Receivers	60 —
3.8	Magnetostrictive Oscillators	62
3.9	Static Characteristics of Magnetostrictive Transducers	64
3.10	Dynamic Characteristics of Magnetostrictive Oscillators	66
3.11	Magnetostrictive Materials	67
3.12	The Design of Magnetostrictive Generators ..	68

CONTENTS

		Page
3.13	Magnetostrictive Receivers	70
3.14	Mechanical Generators	71
3.15	Mechanical Receivers	76
3.16	Electromagnetic Transducers	79
3.17	Electrostatic Transducers	80
3.18	Thermal Transducers	81
3.19	Chemical Detectors	83
3.20	Optical Detectors	84
3.21	Depletion Layer Transducers	85

4. LOW AMPLITUDE PROPAGATION IN GASES

4.1	Velocities in Gases	87
4.2	Absorption and Velocity Dispersion in Gases ..	88
4.3	Classical Theory of Absorption in Gases	88
4.4	Absorption and Velocity Dispersion due to Thermal Relaxation	93
4.5	Simplified Theory of Absorption in Gases due to Thermal Relaxation	95
4.6	Variations of Relaxation Times with Pressure and Temperature	99
4.7	Observations of Absorption and Velocity Dispersion in Gases	99
4.8	Mixtures of Gases	103
4.9	Chemical Reactions	105
4.10	Measurements in Gases	105
4.11	The Acoustic Interferometer	106

5. LOW AMPLITUDE PROPAGATION IN LIQUIDS

5.1	Velocities in Liquids	117
5.2	Absorption and Velocity Dispersion in Liquids ..	118
5.3	Velocities in Liquid Mixtures	123
5.4	Propagation in Media in their Critical States ..	124
5.5	Shear Waves in Liquids	127
5.6	Propagation in Liquid Helium	131
5.7	Measurements in Liquids	133
5.8	Progressive Wave Methods	134
5.9	The Acoustic Interferometer	135
5.10	The Pulse Technique	136
5.11	Optical Methods	137
5.12	The Reverberation Method	140
5.13	Impedance Methods	141
5.14	Hypersonic Waves in Liquids	145

CONTENTS

Page

6. Low Amplitude Propagation in Solids

  6.1 Velocities in Solids 147
  6.2 Ultrasonic Attenuation in Solids 149
  6.3 Losses Characteristic of Polycrystalline Solids .. 150
  6.4 Absorption due to Lattice Imperfections 153
  6.5 Absorption in Ferromagnetic and Ferroelectric Materials 157
  6.6 Absorption due to Electron-Phonon Interactions 160
  6.7 Absorption in Single Crystals due to Thermal Effects 167
  6.8 Absorption due to Other Possible Causes 169
  6.9 Photosensitive Attenuation 171
  6.10 Measurements in Solids 173
  6.11 The Pulse Technique 174
  6.12 Stationary Wave Methods 179
  6.13 Other Methods of Measurement 180
  6.14 Hypersonic Waves in Solids 181

7. Low Power Applications of Ultrasonics

  7.1 General Considerations 185
  7.2 Flaw Detection and Thickness Gauging 185
  7.3 Ultrasonic Delay Lines 189
  7.4 Measurements of Mechanical Stresses 191
  7.5 Ultrasonic Image Converters 192
  7.6 The Ultrasonic Diffraction Grating 193
  7.7 Underwater Applications 194
  7.8 Ultrasonic Applications in Air 194
  7.9 The Ultrasonic Viscometer 195
  7.10 The Ultrasonic Flowmeter 195
  7.11 Pressure Measurements in Fluids 196
  7.12 Medical Applications 196
  7.13 Miscellaneous Applications 197

8. High Energy Ultrasonic Waves

  8.1 General Considerations 199
  8.2 Cavitation 199
  8.3 Emulsification and the Production of Aerosols .. 202
  8.4 The Effects of Ultrasonic Waves on Suspended Particles and Bubbles in Fluids 204
  8.5 Ultrasonic Cleaning 204

CONTENTS

		Page
8.6	Applications to Solids	205
8.7	Metallurgical Applications	206
8.8	Chemical Effects	208
8.9	Biological Effects and Medical Applications ..	209

INDEX 211

FOREWORD

DURING recent years considerable progress has been made in the study of ultrasonics and much literature, including a number of excellent books, has been published. However, the Physics student who requires a reasonably up-to-date general textbook on the subject does not seem to be catered for. It was with this reader in mind that this book has been written.

Whilst it is intended for students in the final years of University Degree and Diploma in Technology courses in Physics, it is hoped that the book will be of use to others who require an introduction to the physical aspects of ultrasonics.

The author is indebted to a number of his colleagues in the Physics Department of Brunel College for their criticisms of the manuscript, to Mrs. M. E. Lorenz for the long hours devoted to its typing, and to Mr. G. E. Haines for his help in preparing some of the illustrations. He also wishes to thank the various sources of information acknowledged in the text.

J. Blitz

1

INTRODUCTION

ULTRASONICS* is the name given to the study and application of sound waves having frequencies higher than those to which the human ear can respond (about 16 kc/s). The subject may be divided into two sections, one dealing with low-amplitude vibrations and the other with high energies. For low-amplitude propagation one is concerned with the effect of the medium on the waves; permanent changes do not take place in the medium. For high-energy applications, however, one is concerned with changes brought about by the waves in the medium.

Basically, low-amplitude waves are passed through a medium in order to measure its propagation constants, i.e. velocity and absorption coefficient. The techniques employed for this purpose are applied to the non-destructive testing of materials (e.g. determination of elastic constants, thickness measurements, and flaw detection) and to instrumentation (e.g. the design of delay lines for computers). Reasons for using ultrasonic frequencies, as opposed to audio-frequencies, include:

(a) shorter wavelengths occur at higher frequencies so that plane wave conditions are more easily realized. This is especially important for small specimens.

(b) absorption coefficients are usually much higher and thus more easily measurable at higher frequencies.

(c) frequencies associated with relaxational phenomena often fall within the ultrasonic range.

High-energy applications include cleaning, drilling, chemical processes, and the production of emulsions. These are carried out either directly by the agitation of the waves or through the phenomenon of cavitation. Some of these operations can be performed at audio-frequencies and quite often the only reason for using ultrasonics is that the process is inaudible. An important advantage of using higher frequency waves is that they are more easily focussed.

One of the first applications of ultrasonics was in 1883 when Galton devised a high-frequency whistle to measure the upper frequency limit of response of the human ear. Even at this time both

* Because of its other meaning in hydrodynamics, the term *supersonics* is no longer used as a synonym for *ultrasonics*.

the piezoelectric and magnetostrictive effects were known but it was not until a sufficient degree of progress was made in the study of electronics that they could be used for the generation of ultrasonics.

The first important use of ultrasonics was made by Langevin during the 1914–18 war for underwater soundings. From then on slow but steady progress was made in the measurements of propagation constants of materials. Early landmarks included Pierce's quartz-driven ultrasonic interferometer in 1925 and the discovery in 1932 by Debye and Sears and also by Lucas and Biquard of the ultrasonic diffraction grating. Pierce's observations of velocity dispersion in carbon dioxide and the work done in 1928 by Herzfeld and Rice on thermal relaxation showed that ultrasonic measurements could produce valuable information about the physical properties of the materials in which the waves were propagated. An important event during the 1930s was the pioneering work of Sokolov in 1934 on ultrasonic flaw detection.

It was not until after the 1939–45 war that any major advances were made in ultrasonics. The discovery of radar led to the development of the pulse technique and its applications to the non-destructive testing of materials and to medical diagnosis. At the same time considerable advances were made in the application of high-energy ultrasonics to industrial and medical processes.

Much scope exists for further developments in both low and high-energy ultrasonics. New materials are now being used for the design of transducers, especially with a view to obtaining higher intensities, and much progress is being made towards the production of very high frequencies comparable with those of the thermal lattice vibrations of materials.

This book, which is intended as an introduction to the subject, is concerned mainly with the physical aspects of ultrasonics. Chapter 2 deals with those parts of acoustic wave theory which are relevant to high frequencies. The third chapter is devoted to a discussion of the various methods of producing and detecting ultrasonics. Chapters 4 to 7 cover the theory and practice of low-amplitude propagation, and in Chapter 8 the reader is introduced to the application of high-energy ultrasonic waves. For more detailed information the reader is recommended to consult the works listed below and the various references given at the end of each chapter.

The author is in favour of using the m.k.s. system of units as far as possible, but there are some circumstances where this system has no particular advantage. Thus quantities such as density are retained in their more familiar c.g.s. forms, and measurements such

2

as length are quoted in terms of suitable orders of magnitude, e.g. 2·71 cm and not 0·0271 metre. Duplication of some mathematical symbols has been unavoidable but confusion should not arise because their meanings are clearly explained in the appropriate parts of the text.

FOR FURTHER READING

General Aspects of Vibrations and Waves
KINSLER, L. E. and FREY, A. R. *Fundamentals of Acoustics*, Wiley, New York/Chapman and Hall, London, 1950
LINDSAY, R. B. *Mechanical Radiation*, McGraw-Hill, New York, 1960
MORSE, P. M. *Vibration and Sound*, McGraw-Hill, New York, 1948
STEPHENS, R. W. B. and BATE, A. E. *Wave Motion and Sound*, Arnold, London, 1950

More General Aspects of Ultrasonics
BERGMANN, L. *Ultrasonics* (trans. H. S. Hatfield), Wiley, New York/Bell, London, 1938 (useful from a historical point of view)
BERGMANN, L. *Der Ultraschall*, 5th Edn., S. Hirzel Verlag, Zurich, 1949 (in German; gives a comprehensive account of the knowledge of the subject up to 1949, excellent for references)
CARLIN, B. *Ultrasonics*, 2nd Edn., McGraw-Hill, New York, 1960 (concentrates on practical aspects)
HUETER, T. F. and BOLT, R. H. *Sonics*, Wiley, New York/Chapman and Hall, London, 1955 (especially useful for its simplified transducer theory)
RICHARDSON, E. G. (ed.), *Technical Aspects of Sound*, Vol. 2, Elsevier, Amsterdam, 1957 (contains sections on transducers and ultrasonic applications)
RICHARDSON, E. G. *Ultrasonic Physics*, 2nd Edn., Elsevier, Amsterdam, 1962

Applications to the Study of the Physical Properties of Materials
COTTRELL, T. L. and McCOUBREY, J. C. *Molecular Energy Transfer in Gases*, Butterworths, London, 1961
HERZFELD, K. F. and LITOVITZ, T. A. *Absorption and Dispersion of Ultrasonics*, Academic Press, New York, 1959 (a comprehensive account of the theory of low-amplitude propagation in gases and liquids)
MASON, W. P. *Physical Acoustics and the Properties of Solids*, van Nostrand, New York, 1958
VIGOUREUX, P. *Ultrasonics*, Chapman and Hall, London, 1950 (more elementary work on propagation in gases and liquids)

Practical Applications
CRAWFORD, A. E. *Ultrasonic Engineering*, Butterworths, London, 1955

GLICKSTEIN, C. *Basic Ultrasonics*, Rider, New York/Chapman and Hall, London, 1960 (practical aspects of the subject clearly explained, with numerous illustrations, at a very elementary level)

Piezoelectricity
CADY, W. G. *Piezoelectricity*, McGraw-Hill, New York, 1946 (monumental work on the theory of piezoelectric crystals)
MASON, W. P. *Piezoelectric Crystals and their Application to Ultrasonics*, van Nostrand, New York, 1949 (deals also with some of the more general aspects of ultrasonics)
VIGOUREUX, P. and BOOTH, C. F. *Quartz Vibrators and their Applications*, H.M.S.O., London, 1950

2

GENERAL PRINCIPLES OF PROPAGATION OF LOW AMPLITUDE WAVES

2.1. GENERAL CONSIDERATIONS

ULTRASONIC propagation constants of materials, i.e. velocity and absorption coefficients, are determined by the use of waves having low amplitudes, for which there is a linear relationship between the applied stress and the resultant strain, i.e. Hooke's law is obeyed. For ease of correlation of the propagation constants of a given substance with its other physical constants, measurements are made as far as possible with plane waves. These originate from a source having a plane surface which vibrates with simple harmonic motion.

Where the source vibrates in the direction of wave motion, longitudinal waves are propagated. These waves give rise to alternate compressions and rarefactions, and for this reason are often called *compression waves*. Where the motion of the source is at right-angles to the direction of wave motion, *transverse waves* are propagated. For a medium in bulk these give rise to alternating shear stresses and the term *shear waves* is often used. Except in special cases to be discussed later, shear waves can be propagated only in solids. It must be made clear that not all transverse waves may be described as shear waves; for example, transverse waves in stretched strings and flexural waves in solid bars are not associated with shear stresses.

2.2. FREE AND FORCED VIBRATIONS

2.2.1. General Considerations

The propagation of sound waves involves the generation of vibrations of the body which provides the source of energy and of the elementary particles in the medium through which the waves are passing. Although these vibrations can take one of a number of different forms, in nearly all cases with which we shall be concerned they can be related to the oscillations of a mass, M, suspended from some fixed support by a spring having a compliance, C_m (i.e. the displacement per unit restoring force). Free vibrations take place when the mass is displaced and then released to oscillate without the aid of any external agency; forced vibrations occur when the mass is

5

caused to undergo sustained oscillations caused by some applied periodic force. A fairly detailed analysis of vibrations has been given by Morse[1] (p. 20) and in this section we are concerned only with the general results.

2.2.2. Free Vibrations

Let the mass, M, be displaced by an amount, x_0, such that the spring is strained within the elastic limit, and then released. The

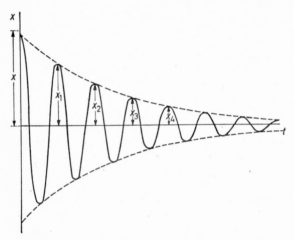

Figure 2.1. Relationship between displacement and time for damped harmonic vibrations

mass, in the absence of damping, will then execute simple harmonic vibrations with a frequency, $f_r = \omega_r/2\pi$, given by the equation:

$$\omega_r = (MC_m)^{-\frac{1}{2}} \tag{2.1}$$

The equation of motion in this instance is:

$$M\frac{\mathrm{d}^2x}{\mathrm{d}t^2} + \frac{x}{C_m} = 0 \tag{2.2}$$

Here, x represents the displacement of the mass at any time, t, and the solution to equation 2.2 is given by:

$$x = x_0 \cos \omega_r t \tag{2.3}$$

where x_0 is called the *displacement amplitude* of the mass.

In practice, frictional effects cause the motion to be damped and, provided that this damping is not too heavy, oscillations still occur but the amplitude decreases with time (see *Figure 2.1*). For small

6

damping the frictional force is proportional to the velocity, the constant of proportionality being R_m, the mechanical resistance. Equation 2.2 is then replaced by the following:

$$M\frac{d^2x}{dt^2} + R_m\frac{dx}{dt} + \frac{x}{C_m} = 0 \tag{2.4}$$

The frequency is lower than that given by equation 2.1 but the difference is usually negligible and can be ignored. To the first order, the solution to 2.4 is:

$$x = x_0 \exp.(-a't) \cos \omega_r t \tag{2.5}$$

where $a' = R_m/2M$.

This equation is represented in *Figure 2.1* as a damped harmonic curve having exponential envelopes. The amplitudes of successive peaks are given by $x_0, x_1, x_2 \ldots x_n$ at times $0, T, 2T \ldots nT$, where $T = 1/f_r$, represents the time period and n is an integer. The logarithmic decrement, δ, is given by the expression:

$$\delta = a'T = R_m T/2M \tag{2.6}$$

and it can be seen that

$$\exp. \delta = \frac{x_0}{x_1} = \frac{x_1}{x_2} = \frac{x_2}{x_3} = \ldots = \frac{x_{n-1}}{x_n} \tag{2.6a}$$

2.2.3. Energy of Free Vibrations

At any given time the total mechanical energy, W_m, of the vibrating system is given by:

$$W_m = \tfrac{1}{2}Mu^2 + \tfrac{1}{2}\frac{x^2}{C_m} \tag{2.7}$$

where $u = dx/dt$ represents the velocity of the mass.

The first term on the right-hand side of equation 2.7 represents the kinetic energy of the mass and the second term the potential energy stored in the spring. In the absence of damping the principle of conservation of energy shows that W_m remains constant at all times. Differentiation of equation 2.3 gives:

$$u = u_0 \sin \omega_r t \tag{2.8}$$

where u_0 represents the velocity amplitude.

From equations 2.3 and 2.8, when $x = 0$, $u = u_0$, and when $u = 0$, $x = x_0$, i.e. when the potential energy of the spring is zero the kinetic energy of the mass assumes its maximum value, $\tfrac{1}{2}Mu_0^2$, and when the potential energy of the spring reaches its maximum value,

$\frac{1}{2}\frac{x_0{}^2}{C_m}$, the kinetic energy of the mass is zero. Hence, we have:

$$W_m = \tfrac{1}{2}Mu_0{}^2 = \tfrac{1}{2}\frac{x_0{}^2}{C_m}$$

Where frictional losses do occur, the energy losses can be related to the logarithmic decrement. By moving the origin a distance $3T/4$ to the right, the curve of *Figure 2.1* represents to a close approximation the variation of u with t. Thus, one can write:

$$\text{exp. } \delta = \frac{u_0}{u_1} = \frac{u_1}{u_2} = \frac{u_2}{u_3} = \ldots = \frac{u_{n-1}}{u_n}$$

The fractional loss of energy per cycle is hence given by:

$$\frac{\Delta W_m}{W_m} = \frac{W_{n-1} - W_n}{W_{n-1}} = 1 - \frac{u_n{}^2}{u_{n-1}{}^2} = 1 - \exp.(-2\delta) \simeq 2\delta \qquad (2.9)$$

where δ is small.

2.2.4. Forced Vibrations

When a periodic force, $F = F_0 \sin \omega t$, of frequency $f = \omega/2\pi$ is applied to the mass, the latter experiences forced oscillations of that frequency and the equation of motion becomes:

$$M\frac{\mathrm{d}^2x}{\mathrm{d}t^2} + R_m\frac{\mathrm{d}x}{\mathrm{d}t} + \frac{x}{C_m} = F_0 \sin \omega t \qquad (2.10)$$

Under steady conditions the velocity, u, at a given time will be:

$$u = \frac{F}{R_m + j(\omega M - 1/\omega C_m)} \qquad (2.11)$$

where $j = (-1)^{\frac{1}{2}}$
and the velocity amplitude is given by:

$$u_0 = \frac{F_0}{\sqrt{R_m{}^2 + (\omega M - 1/\omega C_m)^2}} \qquad (2.12)$$

Equations 2.10, 2.11 and 2.12 are identical in form with those which represent an electrical circuit containing a resistance, R, an inductance, L, and a capacitance, C, in series with an alternating e.m.f., V. Thus R_m, M, C_m and F are analogous to R, L, C and V, respectively, and x and u are equivalent to the electrical charge, Q, and current, i, respectively.
The ratio:

$$Z_m = F/u \qquad (2.13)$$

is consequently termed the *mechanical impedance*.

8

This quantity, as seen from equation 2.11, is complex and may be written as:

$$Z_m = R_m + jX_m \qquad (2.14)$$

where $X_m = (\omega M - 1/\omega C_m)$ is called the *mechanical reactance*.

2.2.5. Resonance

Relationships between velocity amplitude and frequency, as given by equation 2.12, are shown for different values of R_m in *Figure 2.2*.

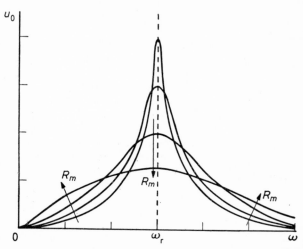

Figure 2.2. Frequency response curves for velocity amplitude with different values of R_m

These are called *frequency response curves* and are similar in form to those for electrical series LRC circuits. The velocity amplitude is a maximum at a frequency, $\omega_r/2\pi = 1/(MC_m)^{\frac{1}{2}}$, where the reactive component of impedance is zero, and resonance is then said to occur. The quality of resonance is described by the *mechanical 'Q' factor*, Q_m, which is defined by the relationship:

$$Q_m = \frac{\omega_r M}{R_m} = \frac{\pi}{\delta} \qquad (2.15)$$

The lower the value of R_m the higher the value of Q_m and hence, the sharper the peaks of the curves. Q_m may be expressed alternatively as follows:

$$Q_m = \frac{\omega_r}{\omega_2 - \omega_1} \qquad (2.15a)$$

9

where ω_1 and ω_2 represent the angular frequencies on either side of ω_r at which the value of the velocity amplitude is reduced to $1/\sqrt{2}$ of its maximum value.

2.3. WAVE VECTORS

The passage of a sound wave through a medium is characterized by *wave vectors*, the values of which vary periodically with both space and time. The most important of these quantities are:

(a) *particle displacement*, ξ, which is the amount of displacement from its mean position of a particle in the medium.

(b) *particle velocity*, $\dot{\xi}$,

(c) *acoustic pressure*, p, which is the change of pressure from the mean value, and

(d) *condensation*, s, the fractional change of density from the mean value.

For plane waves, the wave vectors at any given time have constant values at all points in a given plane normal to the direction of sound propagation. For longitudinal waves they are orientated in the direction of propagation and for transverse waves they are polarized in a direction normal to that of the wave motion.

2.4. THE EQUATION OF MOTION FOR PLANE WAVES

Consider the motion of plane waves at a speed, c, along the x-direction and assume that no attenuation occurs. Particle displacement, ξ, at any time, t, may be represented (see, for example, Wood[2] p. 50) by the equation:

$$\xi = f_1(x - ct) + f_2(x + ct) \tag{2.16}$$

The first expression on the right-hand side refers to waves travelling in the positive direction of x and the second to waves travelling in the negative direction of x. Differentiating this equation twice with respect to x whilst keeping t constant gives:

$$\frac{\partial^2 \xi}{\partial x^2} = f_1''(x - ct) + f_2''(x + ct) \tag{2.17}$$

and with respect to t whilst keeping x constant gives:

$$\frac{\partial^2 \xi}{\partial t^2} = c^2 f_1''(x - ct) + c^2 f_2''(x + ct) \tag{2.18}$$

From equations 2.17 and 2.18 one obtains the general wave equation:

$$\frac{\partial^2 \xi}{\partial t^2} = c^2 \frac{\partial^2 \xi}{\partial x^2} \tag{2.19}$$

10

For propagation in any direction it can be shown that:

$$\frac{\partial^2 \xi}{\partial t^2} = c^2 \left(\frac{\partial^2 \xi}{\partial x^2} + \frac{\partial^2 \xi}{\partial y^2} + \frac{\partial^2 \xi}{\partial z^2} \right) \qquad (2.19a)$$

which may be written as:

$$\frac{\partial^2 \xi}{\partial t^2} = c^2 \nabla^2 \xi \qquad (2.19b)$$

All these equations may be expressed similarly in terms of ξ, p, and s.

For simple harmonic vibrations of the source the wave motion is periodic, and for progressive waves, i.e. those moving in the x is positive direction, equation 2.16 gives:

$$\xi = \xi_0 \sin \left\{ \frac{2\pi}{\lambda}(x - ct) + \phi \right\} \qquad (2.20a)$$

Here ξ_0 represents the displacement amplitude and λ is the wavelength, which can be defined as the distance travelled by the wave during the time period of one complete cycle of vibration of the source. ϕ is an angle which determines the phase of vibration at time $t = 0$. If we put ϕ equal to 180 degrees, this becomes:

$$\xi = \xi_0 \sin (\omega t - kx) \qquad (2.20b)$$

where $\omega = 2\pi f$ is the angular frequency and $k = 2\pi/\lambda$ represents the *wave number*. It is often more convenient to express the variation of ξ in exponential form, viz.:

$$\xi = \xi_0 \exp . j(\omega t - kx) \qquad (2.20c)$$

ξ, p, and s may be expressed in a similar manner.

2.5. THE VELOCITY OF PLANE WAVES

Consider plane longitudinal waves propagated in the x-direction through a homogeneous medium of uniform density, ρ. Let AB (see *Figure 2.3*) represent a thin parallel layer of the medium, with its surfaces A and B normal to the direction of propagation and at respective distances, x, and, $x + \delta x$, from some origin. Now, at some time, t, the wave causes A to be displaced to A′ by an amount, ξ, so that its distance from the origin, along the x-direction is increased to $x + \xi$; this causes B to be displaced to B′. The displacement here, assumed to be small, will then be $\xi + \frac{\partial \xi}{\partial x} \delta x$.

For a cross-section of unit area, the mechanical strain suffered by AB is seen to be $- \partial \xi / \partial x$. If p represents the acoustic pressure

11

which causes this strain we have, in accordance with Hooke's law:

$$\rho = -E\frac{\partial \xi}{\partial x} \qquad (2.21)$$

where E is the appropriate modulus of elasticity for the medium. Now, for sound propagation the strain variations take place so rapidly that there is no time for the system to settle down to a state of thermal equilibrium. Hence, the *adiabatic* value of the elastic

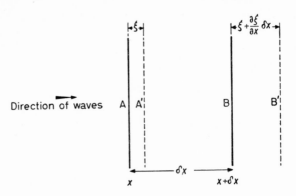

Figure 2.3. Strain on a layer of homogeneous material due to the passage through it of longitudinal plane waves

modulus must be used. Equation 2.21 may be expressed in terms of condensation, s, which is given by:

$$s = \frac{\Delta \rho}{\rho} = -\frac{\Delta v}{v}$$

where $\Delta \rho$ and Δv are the respective density and volume changes caused by the application of p.

i.e. $$s = -\frac{\partial \xi}{\partial x} \qquad (2.22)$$

so that $$p = Es \qquad (2.23)$$

Consider another layer CD, similar to AB, in the medium such that the acoustic pressures at C and D are p and $p + (\partial p/\partial x)\delta x$ respectively. In accordance with Newton's third law of motion equal and opposite pressures act on each of the boundaries C and D. The layer is thus compressed by a pressure $+p$ at C and $-\{p + (\partial p/\partial x)\delta x\}$ at D, so that the resultant acoustic pressure acting on CD is $-(\partial p/\partial x)\delta x$. From Newton's second law of motion this is equal to $\rho\delta x\partial^2\xi/\partial t^2$, hence:

$$\frac{\partial\rho}{\partial x}=-\rho\frac{\partial^2\xi}{\partial t^2} \tag{2.24}$$

equations 2.21 and 2.24 thus give:

$$\frac{\partial^2\xi}{\partial t^2}=\frac{E}{\rho}\frac{\partial^2\xi}{\partial x^2} \tag{2.25}$$

and from equations 2.19 and 2.25 we obtain:

$$c^2=E/\rho \tag{2.26}$$

Equation 2.23 (Hooke's law) can now be expressed alternatively as:

$$p=-\rho c\frac{\partial\xi}{\partial x} \tag{2.27a}$$

or:

$$p=\rho c^2 s \tag{2.27b}$$

If p is considered as the incremental change, ΔP, of the ambient pressure, P, one can re-write equation 2.27b as:

$$P=\rho c^2 s=c^2\Delta\rho$$

or expressing it in differential form, we have:

$$c^2=\left(\frac{\partial P}{\partial\rho}\right)_S \tag{2.28}$$

Here, the subscript, S, indicates a reversible adiabatic change (i.e. constant entropy). Now:

$$\left(\frac{\partial P}{\partial\rho}\right)_S=\frac{E_S}{\rho}\text{ and }\left(\frac{\partial P}{\partial\rho}\right)_T=\frac{E_T}{\rho}$$

where the subscript, T, indicates an isothermal change. It can easily be shown (see, for example, Joos[3] p. 480) that $E_S=\gamma E_T$ where γ is the ratio of the principal specific heats.

Thus,

$$c^2=\gamma\left(\frac{\partial P}{\partial\rho}\right)_T \tag{2.29}$$

A similar method can be used to show that equation 2.26 applies also to shear waves. For shear waves, however, there is no change in volume as a result of the applied stress and, hence, the condensation, s, is always zero. Thus equations 2.22, 2.23, 2.27b, 2.28, and 2.29 have no meaning in this case.

2.6. SPECIFIC ACOUSTIC IMPEDANCE

In Section 2.2.3 the analogy of mechanical vibrations with electrical vibrations was discussed. A similar analogy exists for acoustical and electrical vibrations, for which acoustic pressure, p, particle displacement, ξ, and particle velocity, $\dot{\xi}$, are equivalent to potential difference, electric charge, and current, respectively. One can thus define the *specific acoustic impedance*, Z_a, as the ratio of acoustic pressure to particle velocity, i.e.:

$$Z_a = p/\dot{\xi} \tag{2.30}$$

This is analogous to electrical impedance and is equal to the mechanical impedance per unit area of cross-section of the medium. Like both electrical and mechanical impedances, Z_a is complex and can be expressed as:

$$Z_a = R_a + jX_a \tag{2.31}$$

where R_a and X_a are the resistive and reactive components, respectively.

For plane progressive waves in a non-absorbent medium we have:

$$p = -E\frac{\partial \xi}{\partial x} = -Ef_1'(x-ct) \quad \text{(from equations 2.16 and 2.21)}$$

and:

$$\dot{\xi} = -cf_1'(x-ct) \quad \text{(from equation 2.16) so that}$$

$$Z_a = \frac{p}{\dot{\xi}} = \frac{E}{c} = \rho c \tag{2.32}$$

Here Z_a is real and thus has no reactive component, and the product ρc is the *characteristic impedance* for the particular medium. This quantity, as will be seen in Section 2.11, is a significant factor affecting the reflection and transmission of sound waves.

2.7. RELATIONSHIPS BETWEEN THE WAVE VECTORS OF PLANE WAVES

The particle velocity for plane progressive waves is obtained by differentiating equation 2.20c with respect to t, i.e.:

$$\dot{\xi} = j\omega\xi = j\omega\xi_0 \exp. j(\omega t - kx)$$

or:

$$\dot{\xi} = \dot{\xi}_0 \exp. j(\omega t - kx + \pi/2) \tag{2.23}$$

where $\dot{\xi}_0 = \omega\xi_0$ represents the particle velocity amplitude. From equation 2.32 the acoustic pressure is given by:

$$p = \rho c\dot{\xi} = p_0 \exp. j(\omega t - kx + \pi/2) \tag{2.34}$$

where $p_0 = \rho c\dot{\xi}_0$ is the acoustic pressure amplitude. Equation 2.27 gives a similar relationship for condensation, viz.:

$$s = \frac{p}{\rho c^2} = s_0 \exp. j(\omega t - kx + \pi/2) \tag{2.35}$$

where $s_0 = p_0/\rho c^2$. p, $\dot{\xi}$, and s are seen to be in phase with one another, whereas ξ lags behind them by 90 degrees.

2.8. ACOUSTIC INTENSITY

Sound is a form of energy; the particles of the irradiated medium are set into vibrational motion and possess kinetic energy. Consider some point in the sound field and imagine a very small plane surface, normal to the direction of propagation, having an area, δA, about that point. If δP_m is the rate of flow of energy through that surface, then the ratio $\delta P_m/\delta A$ is defined as the *mean acoustic intensity* over the area, δA. Proceeding to the limit $\delta A \to 0$, we have:

$$I = dP_m/dA$$

where I represents the *acoustic intensity* at that point.

Consider spherical waves propagated in all directions in a uniform non-absorbent medium by a point source having a power, P_m. The intensity at any point at a distance, r, from the source is obtained by dividing the rate of flow of energy, i.e. the power of the source, by the total surface area of a sphere of radius, r, and with the source as centre, i.e.:

$$I = P_m/4\pi r^2.$$

The intensity thus varies with distance in accordance with the inverse square law.

For a plane wave propagated through a uniform non-absorbent medium the principle of conservation of energy shows that I must be the same for all points in the wave. Let E represent the energy density, i.e. the energy per unit volume, of the wave. If the sound energy passes through a unit cross-sectional area with a speed, c, the length of the column of energy flowing in unit time must be equal to c, and the total amount of energy in this column is thus cE. Hence:

$$I = cE.$$

The total mechanical energy of a particle of mass, m, has both kinetic and potential components and, from the principle of conservation of energy, the sum of these is constant at any given time, provided that there is no absorption. When the oscillating particle is passing through its rest position (i.e. $\xi = 0$) its potential energy is zero and its kinetic energy has its maximum value, $\frac{1}{2}m\dot{\xi}_0^2$; this must be the total mechanical energy possessed by the particle. For unit volume of the medium the total mass of the particles is

15

equal to the density, ρ, and the total energy is thus equal to the energy density, E.
Hence:

$$E = \tfrac{1}{2}\rho\dot{\xi}_0{}^2$$

i.e.:
$$I = cE = \tfrac{1}{2}\rho c\dot{\xi}_0{}^2 = \tfrac{1}{2}\dot{\xi}_0{}^2 R_a \qquad (2.36a)$$

where
$$R_a = \rho c \text{ (from equation 2.32)}$$

This equation is analogous to the relationship between the electrical power, P, the current amplitude, i_0, and the resistance, R, i.e.:

$$P = \tfrac{1}{2}i_0{}^2 R$$

Equation 2.36a may be expressed alternatively as:

$$I = \tfrac{1}{2}p_0{}^2/\rho c \text{ (c.f. } P = \tfrac{1}{2}V_0{}^2/R)$$

(where $V_0 = $ voltage amplitude) $\qquad (2.36b)$

$$I = \tfrac{1}{2}p_0\dot{\xi}_0 \text{ (c.f. } p = \tfrac{1}{2}V_0 i_0) \qquad (2.36c)$$

$$I = \tfrac{1}{2}\rho c\omega^2\xi_0{}^2 \qquad (2.36d)$$

or,

$$I = \tfrac{1}{2}\rho c^3 s_0{}^2 \qquad (2.36e)$$

It is seen from the equations 2.36 that acoustic intensity, I, is proportional to the square of the amplitude, A, as represented by either p_0, $\dot{\xi}_0$, ξ_0, or s_0.

Variations of intensity are often expressed in the decibel (dB) scale as follows:

Change in intensity level $= 10 \log_{10}(I_2/I_1)$ dB where I_1 and I_2 represent initial and final intensities, respectively. If A_1 and A_2 are the corresponding amplitudes, it is seen that:

Change in amplitude level $= 20 \log_{10}(A_2/A_1)$ dB.

2.9. PRESSURE OF RADIATION

The relationship between acoustic pressure and particle velocity, as given by equation 2.34, is not a linear one as it may at first appear. This is because the density, ρ, and hence Z_a, must vary periodically in the same way as ρ. It will be shown below that there are two components of pressure, one alternating and the other direct. This is analogous to the electrical case in which both A.C. and D.C. components appear when an alternating voltage is applied across a non-linear resistance.

16

At any given time the density of an element of a medium through which plane longitudinal waves are passing is given by:

$$\rho = \rho_0(1 + s)$$

where s represents the condensation and ρ_0, the static value of the density. The acoustic pressure is then expressed by the equation:

$$p = \rho_0 c\dot{\xi}(1 + s)$$

For sinusoidal variations we may write:

$$\dot{\xi} = \dot{\xi}_0 \sin (\omega t - kx)$$

and

$$s = s_0 \sin (\omega t - kx)$$

Hence,
$$p = \rho_0 c\dot{\xi}_0 \sin (\omega t - kx) [1 + s_0 \sin (\omega t - kx)]$$
$$= \rho_0 c\dot{\xi}_0 \sin (\omega t - kx) + \rho_0 c\dot{\xi}_0 s_0 \sin^2 (\omega t - kx)$$

The average per cycle of the first term on the right-hand side is zero and that of the second term is $\frac{1}{2}\rho_0 c\dot{\xi}_0 s_0$. This second term is the direct component of acoustic pressure and is called the *pressure of radiation*, P_r.

Now, from equation 2.12 we may write:

$$p_0 = \rho_0 c^2 s_0$$

so that
$$P_r = p_0 \xi_0/2c = I/c = E \tag{2.37}$$

i.e., the pressure of radiation is equal in value to the energy density, E.

2.10. ATTENUATION OF PLANE WAVES

Attenuation of plane waves arises from:

(a) deviation of energy from the parallel beam by regular reflection, refraction, diffraction and scattering; and,

(b) absorption, for which mechanical energy is converted into heat by internal friction.

Absorption losses are characteristic of the material through which the waves travel and their evaluation, as will be seen in Chapter 4, can yield valuable information about the physical properties of the medium. Attenuation due to scattering can indicate such factors as grain sizes in polycrystals and the densities and sizes of aerosols and hydrosols. Where attenuation is uniform throughout the acoustic field, it can be characterized by the absorption coefficient, a.

2.10.1. *Absorption Coefficient*

Consider a thin layer of the medium normal to the direction of propagation, at a distance x from an origin and of thickness, dx,

17

see *Figure 2.3*. Where attenuation is uniform, the fractional loss of energy, $2a$, per unit path length, from the layer should be constant (cf. equation 2.9).

Thus: $$dE/E = -2a\,dx$$

and since intensity, I, is directly proportional to energy density, E,

we have: $$dI/I = -2a\,dx$$

By integrating this equation and applying the boundary condition that $I = I_0$, for $x = 0$, one obtains:

$$I = I_0 \exp.(-2ax) \tag{2.38a}$$

or, since I is proportional to the square of the amplitude, A,

$$A = A_0 \exp.(-2ax) \tag{2.38b}$$

where A can be p_0, $\dot{\xi}_0$, ξ_0, etc. Equation 2.20c modified to take absorption into account thus becomes:

$$\xi = \xi_0 \exp.(-ax) \exp. j(\omega t - kx) \tag{2.38c}$$

In equations 2.38, a is defined as the *absorption coefficient* of the medium and is usually expressed in nepers per cm.

Alternatively, absorption may be expressed in terms of the amplitude loss per cycle, i.e. the logarithmic decrement, δ (see Section 2.2.2). This is the custom with damping capacity measurements. It is clearly seen that in this case $\delta = a\lambda$ so that

$$\frac{1}{Q_m} = \frac{\delta}{\pi} = \frac{a\lambda}{\pi} = \frac{2a}{k} \tag{2.38d}$$

Expressing absorption in terms of the decibel scale, as defined in Section 2.8, one can see that one neper is equivalent to 8·686 dB.

2.10.2. *Types of Attenuation*

(a) *Deviation of energy from the parallel beam*

With the exception of scattering, losses due to this cause are, in the main, characteristic of the geometrical configuration of the system. Scattering losses are characteristic of the structure of the material and are dealt with in Section 6.3.2. For Rayleigh type scattering, absorption is proportional to the fourth power of the frequency. Reflection, refraction and diffraction are discussed in Sections 2.11 and 2.12, respectively.

(b) *Hysteretic type of absorption*

Sometimes (see Sections 6.4.3. and 6.5), when periodic adiabatic stresses are applied to a medium, the resultant strain does not vary

18

linearly with the applied stress although Hooke's law may hold for the corresponding stresses under isothermal conditions. The stress/strain curve then takes the form of a hysteresis loop (see *Figure 6.6*), the area of which gives the amount of energy absorbed per half-cycle for unit volume of the material. The loss per cycle is independent of frequency with the result that a increases with frequency in a linear manner.

(c) *Relaxational type of absorption*

The relaxational type of absorption is the one most commonly observed at megacycle frequencies. Consider a small portion of a medium through which sound waves are passing. During the positive half of the stress cycle energy is absorbed, and during the negative

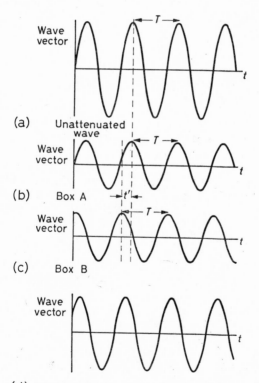

(d) Attenuated wave — resultant of (a) and (c)

Figure 2.4. Phase differences, due to relaxation, between the waveforms in boxes A and B, resulting in attenuation

half of the cycle energy is given up. Usually, a finite period of time is required for this exchange of energy to take place; this is dependent upon the nature of the physical process involved. Litovitz[4] illustrated this phenomenon, as occurring in liquids, by considering the total energy of the liquid as being distributed among a number of compartments, some of which are coupled together in some way. If the temperature of one of them is raised, energy may flow to some of the others until a state of equilibrium is reached. The amount of energy passed to a given compartment grows exponentially with time to a final value and is characterized by a finite time constant, in the same way as the charging of a capacitor through a resistor. This time constant is called the *relaxation time*.

Let compression waves of time period, T, be propagated through a narrow layer such as that illustrated in *Figure 2.3*. Where the applied stress and, hence, the wave vectors in the layer vary sinusoidally with time, the molecules constituting the layer undergo sinusoidal variations of their translational motion, the energy of which may be represented by box, A. Energy transfer from the sound wave to this particular state takes place instantaneously and, if no exchanges occur with the other compartments, the wave-form for box, A is in phase with the sound wave, and no absorption takes place. It may happen, however, that coupling occurs with another box, B, representing some other energy mode (e.g. that of the vibrational motion of the molecules) for which there is a finite time lag before equilibrium conditions are satisfied. Let the wave-form for B be such that the peak occurs at some time, t', later than it does for A (see *Figure 2.4*). The wave-form for B will thus lag in phase by an amount $2\pi(t'/T)$ behind that for A and the resultant wave will suffer a lowering of its peaks and a raising of its troughs, i.e. attenuation will take place.

At low frequencies, for which $t' \ll T$, this phase lag is negligible and the amount of attenuation is very small. As the frequency increases so does the ratio t'/T. The phase lag and, hence, absorption then increase. On the other hand, with increasing frequency the probability of there being sufficient time for all of the energy to enter B from A diminishes, and this factor gives rise to a *decrease* of attenuation with increasing frequency. *Figure 2.5* shows that when the frequency of the wave is increased steadily from a low value, absorption at first increases, rises to a peak at a frequency, f_0, called the *relaxation frequency*, and then diminishes to zero at a frequency so high that there is insufficient time for any energy exchanges at all to occur between boxes A and B in a given cycle. As a result of box B being unable to accept the energy from A the medium becomes 'stiffer' and there is thus an increase in elasticity, E. Consequently the velocity, being equal to $(E/\rho)^{\frac{1}{2}}$, must also increase. This change in velocity with frequency is called *velocity dispersion*.

A simple case of relaxational type of absorption is that due to thermal conduction, which contributes significantly to attenuation in gases. Here the flow of energy is spatial, taking place from regions under compression, at higher temperatures, to those which have expanded and are consequently at lower temperatures. As the frequency increases wavelength diminishes; the temperature gradients are thus increased and the rate of flow of heat from a compressed region to the next rarefied one becomes greater. This contributes towards increasing the entropy of the system and thus gives rise to energy losses. At very high frequencies, however, the

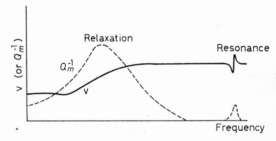

Figure 2.5. Variation of velocity, v, and attenuation, Q_m^{-1}, with frequency (after Litovitz[4])

amount of time available for energy to be able to leave the regions of compression before they become regions of rarefaction diminishes with increase in frequency.

The motion of a particle undergoing forced vibrations of small amplitude is expressed by equation 2.10. If the mass of the particle is very small, one can, at sufficiently low frequencies, ignore the first term on the left-hand side of this equation. The equation then becomes similar in form to that representing the charging of a capacitor, C, through a resistor, R, viz.:

$$V = Q/C + R.\mathrm{d}Q/\mathrm{d}t \qquad (2.39a)$$

and, replacing x by ξ, the modified form of equation 2.10 may be written as:

$$F = \xi/C_m + R_m \mathrm{d}\xi/\mathrm{d}t \qquad (2.39b)$$

from which a relaxation time can be calculated (see Section 2.10.3).

21

Where relaxation effects are negligible, the term, R_m, in equation 2.39b may be ignored and the expression reduces to Hooke's law. At very high frequencies ($f \gg f_0$) the acceleration becomes very high and the first term on the left-hand side of equation 2.10 can no longer be ignored. Thus, at some frequency, f_r, given by $f_r = 1/2\pi(MC_m)^{\frac{1}{2}}$ resonance must occur and there is consequently another absorption peak. This peak, however, covers only a small frequency range and is thus much smaller than the relaxation peak. Inertial effects should cause first a decrease in velocity and then, above the frequency, f_r, an increase in velocity (see *Figure 2.5*).

2.10.3. General Theory of Acoustic Relaxation for Plane Waves

Equation 2.39b represents the motion of a particle undergoing a stress in a medium in which relaxation losses occur, and 2.39a represents the corresponding electrical analogy of the charging of a capacitor through a resistor. If one is to consider the motion of the medium, it is more convenient to express a relationship between acoustic pressure, p, and strain, $S = -\partial\xi/\partial x$, which may be assumed to be linear (see equation 2.27). Except for shear waves, S is the same as the condensation, s, i.e. $p = \rho c^2 S$. By analogy with the equations 2.39 this relationship can be modified to give the expression:

$$p = \rho c^2 S + r \cdot dS/dt \qquad (2.40)$$

where r is a frictional constant. p, S, ρc^2, and r are equivalent to V, Q, $1/C$, and R, respectively. Now the solution to equation 2.39a is:

$$Q = V_0 C\{1 - \exp.\,(-t/RC)\} \qquad (2.41)$$

where V_0 represents the final equilibrium value of V. The solution to equation 2.40 is thus:

$$S = (p'/\rho c^2)\{1 - \exp.\,(-\rho c^2 t/r)\} \qquad (2.42)$$

where p' represents the final steady value of p.

RC and $r/\rho c^2$ are the relaxation times for the expressions 2.41 and 2.42, respectively. The *relaxation time*, τ, is defined as the time taken for the dependent variable to increase from zero to a fraction $(1 - 1/e)$ of its final value. In equation 2.42, $p'/\rho c^2$ is the final steady value of S.

Substituting the relationship, $S = -\partial\xi/\partial x$, into equation 2.40 and then differentiating with respect to x, we have:

$$\frac{\partial p}{\partial x} = -\rho c^2 \frac{\partial^2 \xi}{\partial x^2} - r\frac{\partial^2 \dot{\xi}}{\partial x^2}.$$

Putting $\dfrac{\partial p}{\partial x} = -\rho\,\dfrac{\partial^2 \xi}{\partial t^2}$ (i.e., equation 2.24) into this expression gives:

$$\frac{\partial^2 \xi}{\partial t^2} = c^2\,\frac{\partial^2 \xi}{\partial x^2} + \frac{r}{\rho}\,\frac{\partial^2 \dot{\xi}}{\partial x^2} \qquad (2.43)$$

For simple harmonic waves, the solution is given by equation 2.38c which defines the absorption coefficient a. Substituting the appropriate differential coefficients of ξ from equation 2.38c into equation 2.43, and putting $\tau = r/\rho c^2$ one obtains, after separating the real and imaginary quantities:

$$k^2 - a^2 = 2ka/\omega\tau \qquad (2.44)$$

and

$$2ka = \frac{\omega^3 \tau}{c^2(1 + \omega^2\tau^2)} \qquad (2.45)$$

At this stage we shall define c as representing the velocity of sound at lower frequencies, where relaxation effects are negligible, and $v = \omega/k$ as the velocity at a given frequency, $f = \omega/2\pi$. Equation 2.45 then becomes:

$$a = \frac{\omega^2 \tau v}{2c^2(1 + \omega^2\tau^2)} \qquad (2.46)$$

Substituting this into equation 2.44 produces a quadratic equation for v^2 which, when solved, gives

$$v = \frac{c\sqrt{2}}{\omega\tau}\left[(1 + \omega^2\tau^2)(\sqrt{1 + \omega^2\tau^2} - 1)\right]^{\frac{1}{2}} \qquad (2.47)$$

Equation 2.46 may be rewritten to give the loss per cycle, i.e.

$$Q_m^{-1} = a\lambda/\pi = \frac{v^2 \omega\tau}{c^2(1 + \omega^2\tau^2)} \qquad (2.46a)$$

Thus both attenuation and velocity vary with frequency. Where velocity dispersion is small, the expression, (v^2/c^2), may be regarded as being constant. Hence, maximum absorption occurs when $\omega\tau = 1$ and the relaxation frequency, f_0, is given by:

$$f_0 = \frac{\omega_0}{2\pi} = \frac{1}{2\pi\tau}$$

For frequencies well below the relaxation frequency, i.e. $\omega^2\tau^2 \ll 1$, it is seen that $v \simeq c$ and:

$$a \simeq \frac{\omega^2 \tau}{2c} \qquad (2.46b)$$

i.e. a is proportional to f^2, and:

$$Q_m^{-1} \simeq \frac{\omega\tau}{1 + \omega^2\tau^2} \qquad (2.46c)$$

When a substance has associated with it more than one relaxation time, the curves shown in *Figure 2.5* may have to be modified to show two or more relaxation peaks and their related velocity dispersions. Resonance occurs at much higher frequencies than relaxation, at values usually well beyond the range of acoustic methods. Measurements at such frequencies, which may be of the order of 10^{14} c/s, are normally made with infra-red techniques.

2.11. REFLECTION AND REFRACTION OF PLANE WAVES

2.11.1. *Reflection and Transmission at Normal Incidence to a Plane Boundary Separating Two Media*

Consider a beam of plane waves incident normally to a plane boundary which separates two media, 1 and 2, having characteristic impedances, R_1 and R_2, respectively. In general, part of the incident sound energy is reflected back into medium 1 and the remainder transmitted into medium 2. Let p_i, p_r, and p_t represent values of acoustic pressures for incident, reflected and transmitted waves, respectively, and ξ_i, ξ_r, and ξ_t the corresponding values of particle velocity. If the waves are sinusoidal in form and the medium is non-absorbent, we have:

$$p_i = A_1 \sin (\omega t - k_1 x) = \xi_i R_1 \tag{2.48}$$

$$p_r = B_1 \sin (\omega t + k_1 x) = -\xi_r R_1 \tag{2.49}$$

$$p_t = A_2 \sin (\omega t - k_2 x) = \xi_t R_2 \tag{2.50}$$

The symbols A_1, B_1 and A_2 represent pressure amplitudes and k_1 and k_2 the wave numbers, $2\pi/\lambda$, for the two media. x is positive in the direction of the incident beam. In equation 2.49 the change in signs appended to both x and R_1 indicates that the reflected wave travels in the negative direction of x.

At the boundary, the following conditions must be satisfied at all times:

(a) in order to preserve continuity, the pressure at the boundary must be the same on both sides,

i.e.: $$p_t = p_i + p_r \tag{2.51}$$

(b) particle velocities normal to the boundary must be equal on both sides, otherwise the two media would no longer remain continually in contact with one another, i.e.:

$$\xi_t = \xi_i + \xi_r \tag{2.52}$$

24

Putting $x=0$ at the boundary, equations 2.51 and 2.52 become:

$$A_2 = A_1 + B_1 \tag{2.53}$$

and:

$$R_1 A_2 = R_2(A_1 - B_1) \tag{2.54}$$

Thus:

$$\frac{p_t}{p_i} = \frac{A_2}{A_1} = \frac{2R_1}{R_1 + R_2} \tag{2.55}$$

and:

$$\frac{p_r}{p_i} = \frac{B_1}{A_1} = \frac{R_2 - R_1}{R_1 + R_2} \tag{2.56}$$

Also:

$$\frac{\xi_t}{\xi_i} = \frac{A_2 R_1}{A_1 R_2} = \frac{2R_1}{R_1 + R_2} \tag{2.57}$$

and:

$$\frac{\xi_r}{\xi_i} = -\frac{B_1}{A_1} = \frac{R_1 - R_2}{R_1 + R_2} \tag{2.58}$$

Where R_2 is greater than R_1, i.e. for sound travelling from an acoustically less dense medium to an acoustically denser medium (e.g., from air to a solid), equation 2.56 shows that reflection takes place without any change in phase of acoustic pressure. On the other hand, equation 2.58 shows that a phase change of 180 degrees occurs for particle velocity and, hence, particle displacement. Where, however, R_2 is less than R_1, i.e. radiation passes from a denser to a less dense medium, it is seen that a phase change of 180 degrees takes place for acoustic pressure and no change in phase occurs for particle velocity and, hence, particle displacement.

At the boundary, the ratio of the acoustic intensity of the reflected wave to that of the incident wave defines the *reflection coefficient, a_r,* and the ratio of the intensity of the transmitted wave to that of the incident wave is called the *transmission coefficient, a_t.*

Equations 2.56 and 2.58 thus give:

$$a_r = \left(\frac{R_2 - R_1}{R_1 + R_2}\right)^2 \tag{2.59}$$

and from equations 2.55 and 2.56 we have;

$$a_t = \frac{4R_1 R_2}{(R_1 + R_2)^2} \tag{2.60}$$

These equations show that, where R_1 and R_2 are equal, a_t reaches its maximum value of unity and a_r becomes equal to zero. These are ideal cases but, in practice, good acoustical coupling between the media occurs when R_1 and R_2 have values of the same order of magnitude, i.e. the value of a_t lies between 0·1 and unity. A poor degree of coupling is experienced when the orders of magnitude of

R_1 and R_2 differ considerably, e.g. where a_t may be less than 10^{-3}. Values of R for different materials are given in *Table 2.1*. For example, if the two media are water and steel, for which the respective characteristic impedances are $1 \cdot 4 \times 10^6$ and $4 \cdot 7 \times 10^7$ kg m^{-2} sec^{-1}, a_t has a value of about $0 \cdot 1$, representing a loss of only 10 dB, which

Table 2.1. Characteristic Impedances for Some Commonly Used Materials

The values quoted are for room temperatures and have been obtained mainly from Kaye and Laby[9] and the *Handbook of Chemistry and Physics*[10]

Material	Longitudinal Wave Velocity c m sec^{-1}	Density g cm^{-3}	Characteristic Impedance c kg m^{-2} sec^{-1}
Aluminium	6,400	2·7	$1 \cdot 7 \times 10^7$
Brass	3,500	8·6	$3 \cdot 0 \times 10^7$
Copper	4,700	8·9	$4 \cdot 2 \times 10^7$
Gold	3,700	10·5	$3 \cdot 9 \times 10^7$
Iron	5,900	7·9	$4 \cdot 7 \times 10^7$
Lead	1,200	11·3	$1 \cdot 4 \times 10^7$
Nickel	5,600	8·9	$5 \cdot 0 \times 10^7$
Platinum	3,900	21·45	$8 \cdot 4 \times 10^7$
Silver	3,200	19·3	$6 \cdot 2 \times 10^7$
Steel	6,000	7·8	$4 \cdot 7 \times 10^7$
Barium titanate	5,000	5·4	$2 \cdot 7 \times 10^7$
Quartz (X-cut)	5,700	2·6	$1 \cdot 5 \times 10^7$
Nylon	2,700	1·14	$3 \cdot 0 \times 10^6$
Perspex (Lucite)	2,700	1·2	$3 \cdot 2 \times 10^6$
Glycerol	1,900	1·26	$2 \cdot 4 \times 10^6$
Lubricating oil (approximate values)	1,400	0·8	$1 \cdot 1 \times 10^6$
Olive oil	1,400	0·9	$1 \cdot 3 \times 10^6$
Water	1,500	1·0	$1 \cdot 5 \times 10^6$
Air	330	0·0013	430
Hydrogen	1,300	0·00090	110
Oxygen	320	0·0014	450

means that the two media are reasonably well matched. If, on the other hand, the water is replaced by air, for which R has a value of only 400 kg m^{-2} sec^{-1}, a_t is reduced to about 10^{-6}, which corresponds to a loss of 60 dB; this is an example of extremely poor coupling. Matching may be improved by placing a third medium in between, as shown in the following section.

2.11.2. Transmission at Normal Incidence Through Three Media Separated by Plane Parallel Boundaries

It may be shown (see, for example, Kinsler and Frey[5], p. 152) that when a parallel layer of a third medium, having a characteristic impedance, R', is placed in between the media 1 and 2 the value of a_t is given by the expression:

$$a_t = \frac{4R_1 R_2}{(R_1 + R_2)^2 \cos^2 k'l + (R' + R_1 R_2/R')^2 \sin^2 k'l} \qquad (2.61)$$

where k' is the wave-number for the intervening medium.

Three special cases are considered here:

(a) where the intermediate medium is sufficiently thin that $k'l \ll 1$, the cosine term in equation 2.61 tends to unity and the sine term becomes negligible. The expression reduces to equation 2.60 and the intervening medium should then have no effect on the transmission of sound. The value of l required to satisfy this condition depends upon the relative values of R_1, R_2, and R', and where R' is very small compared with R_1 and R_2 this approximation is not justified.

Consider, for example, the case of the radiating surface of a quartz crystal transducer placed in direct contact with a steel surface which is machined to a tolerance of 2 microns. The two solid surfaces are in contact with one another in a few places only and we have, in effect, three consecutive media, quartz, air and steel. The corresponding values of R_1, R', and R_2 are approximately $1 \cdot 5 \times 10^7$, 400 and $4 \cdot 7 \times 10^7$ kg m^{-2} sec^{-1}, respectively. The thickness of the intervening medium is 2×10^{-4} cm and, for a frequency of 1 Mc/s, the value of k' would be approximately 200 cm^{-1}. Equation 2.61 shows that the approximate value of a_t would be as low as 4×10^{-9}. This compares with a value of $0 \cdot 76$ obtained from equation 2.60. On the other hand, if a film of water of characteristic impedance $1 \cdot 5 \times 10^6$ kg m^{-2} sec^{-1} intervenes between the two solid surfaces, so that k' is approximately 42 cm^{-1}, the value of a_t as given by equation 2.61 approximates very closely to that given by equation 2.60, i.e. the effect of the coupling fluid on the sound transmission can be ignored.

(b) where the thickness of the intervening medium is an integral number of half-wavelengths, i.e. $l = n\lambda/2$ or $k'l = n\pi$, equation 2.61 again reduces to the form of equation 2.60. The value of the transmission coefficient is then given exactly by this equation so that it is independent of the characteristic impedance of the intervening layer. At upper ultrasonic frequencies, a high degree of precision is

27

required for the preparation of the boundary surfaces in order to achieve this condition.

(c) where the thickness of the intervening medium is equal to an odd number of quarter-wavelengths, i.e. $l = (2n - 1)\lambda/4$ or $k'l = (2n - 1)\pi/2$, equation 2.61 reduces to the following form:

$$a_t = \frac{4R_1 R_2}{(R' + R_1 R_2/R')^2} \qquad (2.61a)$$

If the characteristic impedance of the intermediate layer has a value such that $R'^2 = R_1 R_2$, it is seen that $a_t = 1$, i.e. 100 per cent transmission occurs. This has an analogy in optics with the 'blooming' of lenses, i.e. coating their surfaces with quarter-wavelength layers. Where the value of R' is negligible compared with the values of R_1 and R_2, e.g. when the intervening medium is air, the transmission coefficient tends to zero. This is applied to the quarter-wavelength backing of crystal transducers (see Sections 3.4 and 4.10.3) for which no transmission of energy takes place from their 'non-radiating' surfaces.

2.11.3. Reflection and Refraction at Oblique Incidence to a Plane Boundary Separating Two Media

Figure 2.6 illustrates a longitudinal ray, XY, incident on a plane boundary separating media 1 and 2, Y being the point of incidence on the boundary. YW and YZ are the respective reflected and refracted longitudinal waves. Where one or both of the media supports a shear stress, mode conversion will take place at the boundary. This is because the acoustic pressure for the incident longitudinal waves is directed obliquely to the boundary and can thus be resolved into two components, one acting along the boundary and the other at right-angles to it. The layers of the media at the boundary are therefore subjected to both compressive and shear stresses with the result that, where appropriate, shear waves as well as longitudinal waves are reflected and transmitted. The shear waves are polarized in the plane containing the longitudinal wave vectors, i.e. the plane of incidence. In *Figure 2.6* the reflected and transmitted shear waves are represented by the rays YW' and YZ', respectively.

The velocities and directions of the various waves are given, in accordance with simple wave theory and Snell's law, by:

$$c_1/\sin\ \theta_1 = c'_1/\sin\ \theta'_1 = c_2/\sin\ \theta_2 = c'_2/\sin\ \theta'_2 \qquad (2.62)$$

Here, c_1 and c_2 represent the longitudinal wave velocities in media 1 and 2, respectively, and c'_1 and c'_2 represent the corresponding shear wave velocities. θ_1 represents both the angles of incidence and reflection and θ_2 the angle of refraction for the longitudinal waves. θ'_1 and θ'_2 represent, respectively, the angles of reflection and refraction for the shear waves.

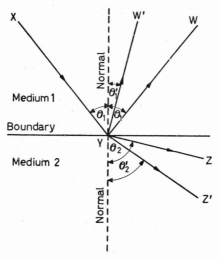

Figure 2.6. Reflection and refraction of a beam of longitudinal waves incident to a plane boundary separating two media

The author is unaware of any method of calculating the values of a_t and a_r for the general case, but where mode conversion does not occur, e.g. where both media do not support shear stresses, it may be shown (see, for example, Kinsler and Frey[5], p. 147) that:

$$a_r = \left(\frac{R_2 \cos \theta_1 - R_1 \cos \theta_2}{R_2 \cos \theta_1 + R_1 \cos \theta_2}\right)^2 \tag{2.63a}$$

$$a_t = \frac{4R_1 R_2 \cos \theta_1 \cos \theta_2}{(R_2 \cos \theta_1 + R_1 \cos \theta_2)^2} \tag{2.63b}$$

Two important occurrences of mode conversion may be mentioned. The first is in the propagation of shear waves in solids. Let us suppose that c_2 is greater than c_1, so that the refracted longitudinal waves are deviated away from the normal, i.e. θ_2 is greater than θ_1. This is generally the case where medium 1 is a liquid and medium 2 a solid. Furthermore c'_2 is always less than c_2 (see Section 6.1). When the angle of incidence, θ_1, is increased to its first critical value, the refracted longitudinal ray, YZ, is directed along the boundary (see *Figure 2.7a*), i.e. $\theta_2 = 90°$. At greater angles of incidence the longitudinal waves are totally reflected and only shear waves are transmitted through medium 2. Where the transverse wave velocity in medium 2 is greater than the incident longitudinal wave velocity, which is usual for transmission from liquids into solids, θ'_2 is greater than θ_1. Thus the refracted shear waves are also deviated away from the normal. When θ_1 is increased to its

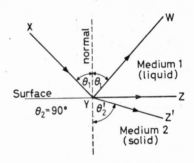

(a) θ_1 equal to its first critical value

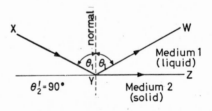

(b) θ_1 equal to its second critical value

Figure 2.7. The use of mode conversion to propagate (*a*) shear waves and (*b*) surface waves through a solid

second critical value, the shear waves, YZ', travel along the boundary as *surface waves* (see *Figure 2.7b*).

Mode conversion also occurs in a long solid rod immersed in a fluid medium. Imagine a crystal source placed at one end of this rod (see *Figure 2.11*). At a certain distance from the source, provided that the rod is long enough, the beam starts to spread out, i.e. Fraunhofer diffraction occurs (see Section 2.12). When the diffracted rays reach the side walls, the reflected beams consist of both shear waves and longitudinal waves, which travel at different speeds in accordance with equation 2.62. For the pulse method of measuring propagation constants (see Section 6.11) this phenomenon may give rise to spurious indications.

2.11.4. Stationary Waves

For reflection at normal incidence to a plane boundary, the incident and reflected waves in medium 1 interfere with one another. The resultant acoustic pressure, p, at any point in this medium is given by the expression:

$$p = p_i + p_r$$

and the corresponding particle velocity, ξ, by the equation:

$$\xi = \xi_i + \xi_r$$

From equations 2.48 and 2.49, these may be rewritten as follows:

$$p = A_1 \sin (\omega t - k_1 x) + B_1 \sin (\omega t + k_1 x)$$

and:
$$\xi = \frac{A_1}{R_1} \sin (\omega t - k_1 x) - \frac{B_1}{R_1} \sin (\omega t + k_1 x) \qquad (2.64)$$

assuming that the medium is non-absorptive. At the boundary, where $x = 0$, the pressure amplitude, p_0, and the velocity amplitude, ξ_0, are expressed respectively as:

$$p_0 = A_1 + B_1$$

and:
$$\xi_0 = (A_1 - B_1)/R_1$$

The values of p_0 and ξ_0 at various distances from the boundary will depend upon the relative values of R_1 and R_2.

Let p_{0i} and ξ_{0i} represent the respective values of pressure and particle velocity amplitudes for the incident waves and p_{0r} and ξ_{0r} the corresponding values for the reflected waves.

(i) where R_2 is greater than R_1

Equation 2.56 shows that no change in phase occurs upon reflection for p whereas equation 2.58 indicates that a phase change of 180 degrees takes place for ξ. We thus have that:

$$A_1 = +p_{0i} = +\xi_{0i} R_1$$

and:
$$B_1 = +p_{0r} = -\xi_{0r} R_1$$

From equations 2.64 it is seen that, at the boundary ($x = 0$) and at distances equal to an integral number, n, of half-wavelengths from it ($x = -n\lambda/2$), there occur *maximum* values of p_0 and *minimum* values of ξ_0, and, hence, also *minimum* values of displacement amplitude, ξ_0. At points midway between these positions, i.e.

31

$x = -(2n+1)\lambda/4$ the values of p_0 are minimum and those of both ξ_0 and $\dot{\xi}_0$ are maximum.

(ii) *where R_2 is less than R_1*

Upon reflection, a phase change of 180 degrees occurs for p but no phase changes for $\dot{\xi}$ and ξ. Thus:

$$A_1 = +p_{0i} = +\dot{\xi}_{0i}R_1$$

and:
$$B_1 + -p_{0r} = +\dot{\xi}_{0r}R_1$$

Equations 2.64 show that at the boundary ($x = 0$) and also for $x = -n\lambda/2$ the values of p_0 are *minimum* and those of both $\dot{\xi}_0$ and ξ_0 are *maximum*. For $x = -(2n+1)\lambda/4$ *maximum* values of p_0 and *minimum* values of $\dot{\xi}_0$ and ξ_0 are to be found.

The ratio of the maximum to minimum values of amplitude is called the *standing wave ratio* (S.W.R.), which is given by the expression:

$$\text{S.W.R.} = \frac{p\max.}{p\min.} = \frac{p_{0i} + p_{0r}}{p_{0i} - p_{0r}}$$
$$= \frac{\dot{\xi}\max.}{\dot{\xi}\min.} = \frac{\dot{\xi}_{0i} + \dot{\xi}_{0r}}{\dot{\xi}_{0i} - \dot{\xi}_{0r}}$$

This is seen to equal the ratio R_2/R_1 or R_1/R_2, whichever is the greater. Thus from equations 2.59 and 2.60 corresponding values of reflection and transmission coefficients, respectively, may be obtained.

Where the reflection coefficient is effectively 100 per cent, as one would find for a solid-gas boundary, we have $p_{0i} = p_{0r}$ and $\dot{\xi}_{0i} = \dot{\xi}_{0r}$, with the result that A and B are numerically equal to one another. Equations 2.64 may then be rewritten as:

$$p_0 = 2\, p_{0i} \cos k_1 x$$

and:
$$\xi_0 = 2\, \dot{\xi}_{0i} \sin k_1 x \tag{2.64a}$$

The maximum values of p_0, $\dot{\xi}_0$, and ξ_0 then become equal to $2p_0$, $2\dot{\xi}_0$, and $2\xi_0$, respectively, and the corresponding minimum values are all equal to zero. The positions of the maxima are termed *antinodes* and those of the minima are called *nodes*. Thus the pressure nodes occur at velocity and displacement antinodes and the pressure antinodes at the velocity and displacement nodes.

Where absorption occurs in the medium, equations 2.64 are modified to become:

$$p = A_1 \exp.(-a_1 x) \sin(\omega t - k_1 x) + B_1 \exp.(+a_1 x) \sin(\omega t + k_1 x)$$

$$\xi = \frac{A_1}{R_1} \exp.(-a_1 x) \sin(\omega t - k_1 x) - \frac{B_1}{R_1} \exp.(+a_1 x) \sin(\omega t + k_1 x)$$
$$\tag{2.64b}$$

where a_1 is the absorption coefficient for medium 1. Here, A_1 and B_1 are replaced by A_1 exp. $(-a_1 x)$ and B_1 exp. $(+a_1 x)$ respectively.

2.11.5. Stationary Waves in Bounded Media

In many applications one is concerned with the behaviour of sound waves in a bounded medium, such as a solid rod or an air column contained in a tube closed at both ends. Let us consider such a bounded medium of length, l, where the end boundaries are normal to the direction of propagation. Let a represent the absorption coefficient of the medium and exp. 2β and exp. 2γ the reflection coefficients, as defined by equation 2.63a, at the boundaries, $x = 0$, and $x = l$, respectively. Also assume that the pressure amplitude of the progressive wave is p_{0i} at $x = 0$, and that the characteristic impedance of the medium is less than that beyond either boundary. If the variation of p is expressed in the form exp. $j(\omega t - kx)$, it can be seen by taking into account successive reflections at both ends, that the pressure amplitude, p_0, at any point is given by:

$$p_0 = p_{0i} \{ \exp. [-(a+jk)x] + \exp. (\beta+\gamma) \exp. [-(a+jk)(x+2l)]$$
$$+ \exp. 2 (\beta+\gamma) \exp. [-(a+jk)(x+4l)]$$
$$+ \exp. 3 (\beta+\gamma) \exp. [-(a+jk)(x+6l)]$$
$$+ \ldots \ldots \ldots \ldots \ldots$$
$$+ \exp. \beta \exp. [-(a+jk)(2l-x)]$$
$$+ \exp. (2\beta+\gamma) \exp. [-(a+jk)(4l-x)]$$
$$+ \exp. (3\beta+2l) \exp. [-(a+jk)(6l-x)]$$
$$+ \ldots \ldots \ldots \ldots \ldots$$
$$= p_{0i} \frac{\exp. [-(a+jk)x] + \exp. [-(a+jk)(2l-x)] \exp. \beta}{1 - \exp. (\beta+\gamma) \exp. [-(a+jk)2l]} \qquad (2.65)$$

At the boundary, where $x = 0$, we have:

$$p = p_{0i} \frac{1 + \exp. [-(a+jk)2l] \exp. \beta}{1 - \exp. [-(a+jk)2l] \exp. (\beta+\gamma)} \qquad (2.65a)$$

This equation is used in the theory of the acoustic interferometer (see Section 4.10) in which one considers the effects of the reaction of the stationary wave system on the source, which is usually a quartz crystal plate. Assuming that the source is at $x = 0$ and the reflector at $x = l$, the pressure amplitude at the source is given by equation 2.65a.

Where the medium in which measurements are made is a gas, both β and γ may be equated to zero. Equation 2.65 reduces to:

$$p_0 = p_{0i} \frac{\cosh (a+jk)(l-x)}{\sinh (a+jk)l} \qquad (2.65b)$$

and the pressure amplitude at the source is thus given by the expression:

$$p_0 = p_{0i} \coth (a + jk)l \qquad (2.65c)$$

The above expression is complex and it may be expressed more conveniently as:

$$p_0 = p_{0i} \frac{\sinh 2al - j \sin 2kl}{\cosh 2al - \cos 2kl} \qquad (2.66)$$

This may be written as:

$$p_0 = p_{0i}(A + jB) \qquad (2.66a)$$

where

$$A = \frac{\sinh 2al}{\cosh 2al - \cos 2kl}$$

and

$$B = \frac{\sin 2kl}{\cosh 2al - \cos 2kl}$$

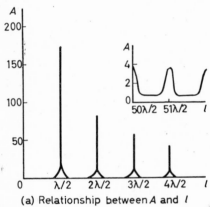

(a) Relationship between A and l

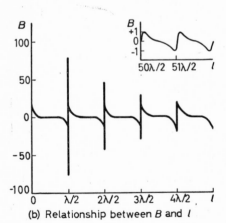

(b) Relationship between B and l

Figure 2.8. Relationships between A, B, and l in accordance with equations 2.66, for $a = 0 \cdot 01$ neper cm^{-1} and $\lambda = 0 \cdot 12$ cm (after Hubbard[8])

It is clear that the expression, $A - jB$, being complex, must be some function of the specific acoustic impedance of the medium in the interferometer. Variations of both A and B with l are illustrated in *Figure 2.8*. Where the value of l is such that resonance occurs, i.e. $l = n\lambda/2$, n being an integer, the impedance is entirely resistive. Here A reaches its peak values and B passes through zero, accompanied by a change of sign.

2.12. DIFFRACTION

For a point source of acoustic energy, radiation is emitted equally in all directions and the wavefronts are spherical. In practice, however, extended sources are used; these may be taken as equivalent to a large number of point sources situated very close together.

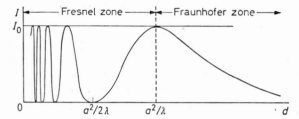

Figure 2.9. Variation of intensity along the axis of a circular source vibrating as a piston

The nature of the resultant wavefronts can be deduced by applying Huygens' principle for which interference with one another of the 'wavelets' originating from each of the point sources is considered. For a circular source of radius, a, having a plane radiating surface oscillating as a piston with a simple harmonic motion, it can be shown (see, for example, Kinsler and Frey[5], p. 185) that the variation of intensity, I, with distance, d, along the axis is given by the equation:

$$I = I_0 \sin^2[(\pi/\lambda)\{(d^2 + a^2)^{\frac{1}{2}} - d\}] \qquad (2.67)$$

where I_0 represents the maximum value of I. It is seen that $I = 0$ when $(d^2 + a^2)^{\frac{1}{2}} - d = n\lambda$, and $I = I_0$ when $(d^2 + a^2)^{\frac{1}{2}} - d = (2n+1)\lambda/2$, where n is an integer.

The variation of I with d (see *Figure 2.9*) shows a number of peaks, the spacing of which increases with distance from the source. Putting $n = 0$ and $n = 1$, respectively, we see that the two final zero values of intensity occur when $d = \infty$ and $d \simeq a^2/2\lambda$ where $d \gg a$.

The final maximum is found where $d \simeq a^2/\lambda$, assuming that $d \gg a$, for which $n = 0$.

The region between the source and the position of the final intensity maximum is described as the *Fresnel* or near zone and that beyond is the *Fraunhofer* or far zone. In the Fresnel zone the beam is parallel and in the *Fraunhofer* zone the beam diverges so as to appear to originate from the centre of the source (see *Figure 2.10*).

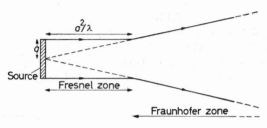

Figure 2.10. Configuration of a beam of sound in front of a circular source vibrating as a piston

The intensity in the far zone falls off with distance in accordance with the inverse square law. This can be seen from equation 2.67, i.e. by putting $d \gg a$, we have:

$$\sin[(\pi/\lambda)\{(d^2 + a^2)^{\frac{1}{2}} - d\}] \simeq \pi a^2/2d.$$

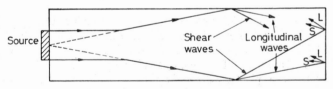

Figure 2.11. Mode conversion on the reflection of a diffracted wave at the surfaces of a rod

In the near zone the variations of intensity with distance along lines parallel with the axis, i.e. not passing through the centre of the source, will be different from that along the axis. This fact can be appreciated from a consideration of the Principle of Conservation of Energy, because the average intensity for all given cross-sections of the beam must be constant. This intensity variation is important for the application of the pulse technique to flaw detection in materials (see Section 7.2), in that should the position of a small defect coincide with that of a minimum value of intensity it is likely that its presence may not be observed.

The occurrence of Fraunhofer diffraction presents difficulties when measurements of propagation constants are conducted. The diffracted beam contains energy removed from the main beam and errors thus occur in the measurements of absorption coefficients. Furthermore, where the diffracted beam is reflected at the lateral boundaries of the medium back into the main beam, spurious indications may be observed (see, for example, *Figure 2.11*). Experimental errors caused by Fraunhofer diffraction are discussed more fully in Section 4.11.2. These errors may be reduced by arranging, as far as possible, that measurements are confined to the Fresnel zone.

2.13. ACOUSTIC WAVEGUIDES

The condition that plane waves are propagated into the Fresnel zone for a plane source is that the latter vibrates as a piston. This may not always occur; for example, where a quartz crystal is not properly mounted there may be a variation in phase over its radiating surface. There may thus be a component of the sound wave in a direction at right-angles to that of propagation. Non-piston like vibrations can occur also for a crystal radiating into a solid via a coupling medium of non-uniform thickness.

Where the medium has finite lateral boundaries, the lateral components of the waves will be reflected from side to side, i.e. the medium acts as a waveguide. For stationary waves, nodes and antinodes will be observed in the lateral direction as well as in the forward direction; these are sometimes called *Rayleigh cross-modes* (see, for example, Richardson[6], p. 75).

2.14. FOCUSSING SYSTEMS

The focussing of ultrasonic energy is normally obtained by means of either a curved transducer arrangement or an acoustic lens. For the former the energy is brought to a focus at its centre of curvature. A curved transducer arrangement may consist of either a single concave ceramic transducer or a mosaic placed on a concave surface (see Section 3.6.2).

An acoustic lens is designed in the same way as an optical lens, and its focal length, f_L, is related to its properties by the expression:

$$\frac{1}{f_L} = \left| \frac{c - c_L}{c_L} \right| \left(\frac{1}{r_1} + \frac{1}{r_2} \right) \tag{2.68}$$

Here r_1 and r_2 represent the radii of curvature of the lens surfaces, c the velocity of sound in the liquid, and c_L the velocity of sound in the lens.

By considering the expression, $\left| \dfrac{c - c_L}{c_L} \right|$, as being always a positive quantity, the value of r_1 or r_2 is positive when the convex surface faces the medium in which the speed of sound is greater. This is equivalent to the real-is-positive convention used in optics. Equation 2.68 is valid only for paraxial rays. For optimum coupling conditions the characteristic impedances of the lens and liquid should have the same orders of magnitude. For a lens made of Perspex, for which the density is $1 \cdot 2$ g cm^{-3} and the acoustic velocity 2,800 m sec^{-1}, the transmission coefficient for each surface is about 75 per cent when it is placed in water. Using a plano-concave system for which the radius of curvature is 10 cm, a converging lens having a focal length of 17 cm is obtained. This convergence is in contrast with the effect of a glass optical lens in air where a plano-concave system is divergent.

2.15. THE DOPPLER EFFECT

Where the source, receiver, or both are moving, a change of frequency may be observed. This is due to the Doppler effect. For the simplest case where the source is moving with a velocity, u, towards the receiver moving with a velocity, v, in the same direction, it can be shown (see, for example, Stephens and Bate[7], p. 146) that the frequency change, Δf, is given by the expression:

$$\Delta f = \left(\frac{c - v}{c - u} - 1 \right) f \qquad (2.69)$$

where f and c represent the frequency and velocity, respectively, of the sound waves. Thus, for a moving source and a stationary receiver, $v = 0$ and:

$$\Delta f = \pm \frac{u}{c - u} f \qquad (2.69a)$$

The positive sign denotes that the source is moving towards the receiver. For a stationary source, $u = 0$ and:

$$\Delta f = \pm \frac{v}{c} f \qquad (2.69b)$$

Here the positive sign indicates that the receiver is moving towards the source.

Where both source and receiver are stationary but the waves are reflected back by an obstacle moving with a velocity, w, the effect is the same as if the receiver were moving with a velocity, $2w$, and the change in frequency is given by the expression:

$$\Delta f = \pm \frac{2w}{c} f \qquad (2.70)$$

The Doppler effect is also observed when the medium is moving but both source and receiver may be stationary. If the medium is moving with a velocity, Δc, the effective acoustic velocity is increased or decreased by this amount. The frequency, however, remains constant, and the change in velocity is indicated by a change in wavelength.

In all cases considered in this section it is assumed that the velocities act along the same straight line. Where this is not so, the expressions are more complicated.

REFERENCES

1. MORSE, P. M. *Vibration and Sound*, 2nd Edn., McGraw-Hill, New York, 1948
2. WOOD, A. *Acoustics*, Blackie, London, 1940
3. JOOS, G. *Theoretical Physics*, Blackie, London, 1934
4. LITOVITZ, T. A. *J. acoust. Soc. Amer.*, 1959, **31**, 681
5. KINSLER, L. E. and FREY, P. *Fundamentals of Acoustics*, Wiley, New York/Chapman and Hall, London, 1950
6. RICHARDSON, E. G. *Ultrasonic Physics*, 2nd Edn., Elsevier, Amsterdam, 1962
7. STEPHENS, R. W. B. and BATE, A. E. *Wave Motion and Sound*, Arnold, London, 1950
8. HUBBARD, J. C. *Phys. Rev.*, 1931, **38**, 1011
9. KAYE, G. W. C. and LABY, T. H. *Tables of Physical and Chemical Constants*, 11th Edn., Longmans Green, London, 1957
10. *Handbook of Chemistry and Physics*, Chemical Rubber Company, Cleveland, Ohio—published annually

3

ULTRASONIC GENERATORS AND RECEIVERS

3.1. INTRODUCTION

SOUND waves are generated or received by a device called a *transducer*; this converts energy from one form to another. Thus acoustic transducers are used to transfer acoustical energy to or from such forms of energy as electrical, mechanical, and thermal. A *reversible transducer* is one which can convert energy in either direction.

The various types of transducer are discussed here under the following headings:

(*i*) *Crystal oscillators*: These utilize the *piezoelectric effect*, which is reversible. The range of frequencies used is very wide, the upper limit being about 10,000 Mc/s.

(*ii*) *Magnetostrictive oscillators*: These devices make use of the phenomenon of *magnetostriction*, which is also reversible. The upper frequency limit is of the order of 100 kc/s.

(*iii*) *Purely mechanical generators and receivers*: Under this heading fall such instruments as whistles and sirens, which are used as generators, and radiometers and Rayleigh discs, which act as receivers. The upper frequency limit for mechanical transducers is also about 100 kc/s.

(*iv*) *Electromagnetic transducers*: These instruments are widely used as loudspeakers and microphones in the audio-frequency range but have very limited application at ultrasonic frequencies. They have been used at frequencies at the lower end of the ultrasonic range for high power generation, and up to 50 kc/s for low power applications.

(*v*) *Electrostatic transducers*: These devices have been used at frequencies below 100 kc/s for internal friction measurements and they have also been employed as condenser microphones.

(*vi*) *Miscellaneous transducers*: Under this heading may be placed devices, mainly receivers, for which conversion takes place between acoustical and some form of energy other than electrical and mechanical, e.g. chemical or thermal energy.

Ultrasonic receivers may be considered as falling into one of two classes:

(*a*) *Receivers terminating ultrasonic lines*: This class includes

40

crystal transducers used for the measurements of propagation constants and for the various applications of these measurements. It also includes devices for measuring the overall energy dissipated in a sound field.

(b) *Receivers inserted as probes*: Transducers falling into this category are often called ultrasonic microphones or hydrophones and they are used to measure intensities or other acoustic characteristics in fluids. An important consideration is that the insertion of the receiver probe does not interfere with the configuration of the waves. To satisfy this condition the dimensions of the microphone should be small compared with wavelength. Ideally, the diameter of a probe should be less than 0.1λ but where a high degree of accuracy is not essential, this may be increased somewhat. However, the use of probe microphones is normally limited to the lower frequency range.

3.2. CRYSTAL OSCILLATORS

Two types of crystal may be used for generating ultrasonic waves, one which displays the *piezoelectric effect* and the other the *electrostrictive effect*.

3.2.1. *The Piezoelectric Effect*

The piezoelectric effect, which was first discovered by the Curie brothers in 1880, occurs in crystals having axes of non-symmetry. Let a slab or disc of such a crystal be cut with its parallel surfaces lying normal to an axis of non-symmetry. On subjecting this slab to a mechanical stress, equal and opposite electric charges appear on the parallel surfaces. Provided that the crystal is not strained beyond its elastic limit, the magnitude of the charge density (or dielectric polarization) is directly proportional to the applied stress.

The converse effect was predicted by Lippmann in 1881 and discovered experimentally by the Curie brothers in the same year. When an electric field is applied in the direction of an axis of non-symmetry the slab is mechanically strained, the amount of strain being proportional to the intensity of the applied field. From a consideration of the principle of conservation of energy the direct and converse piezoelectric effects may be shown to be equal and opposite.

These effects are prominent in crystals such as quartz, Rochelle salt, tourmaline and lithium sulphate. Quartz, which is commonly used for ultrasonic propagation, belongs to the trigonal system and a typical specimen is illustrated in *Figure 3.1*. It can be seen from

41

this diagram that the Z-axis, the optic axis, is one of symmetry and that a section through the main body of the crystal, normal to the Z-axis, is hexagonal in shape. The three axes joining opposite edges are known as the X-axes and the corresponding axes perpendicular to these, i.e. joining opposite faces, are called the Y-axes. These are not axes of symmetry and slabs cut with their faces perpendicular to them display the piezoelectric effect. Crystals cut with their faces normal to an X- or Y-axis are called X- or Y-cuts, respectively. X-cut crystals are normally used for the

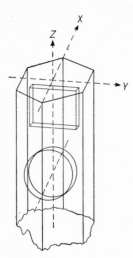

Figure 3.1. X-cut rectangular and circular plates from a quartz crystal

propagation of compressional waves and Y-cut crystals are often used for the generation of shear waves. Details of other crystal cuts, together with their applications, have been given by Vigoureux and Booth.[1]

Consider an X-cut quartz crystal in the shape of a rectangular prism, as shown in *Figure 3.1*. An electric field applied along the X-axis in a given direction produces a compression in that direction. At the same time an expansion takes place along the Y-direction. On reversing the direction of the field an expansion occurs along the X-axis and a compression along the Y-axis; no strain is observed in the direction of the Z-axis. Let a pair of surfaces normal to either the X- or Y-axes be coated with some conducting material to form electrodes. When an alternating voltage of frequency, f, is applied across them, small-amplitude oscillations of the crystal occur. The amplitude is increased considerably when f coincides with one of the natural frequencies of mechanical vibration for the particular axis. In practice these crystals are operated at a resonant frequency for either 'thickness' or 'length' vibrations, depending on whether resonance occurs for the direction perpendicular to or parallel with the radiating faces. The natural frequency for mechanical vibrations varies inversely with the dimension along which they occur; lower frequencies are thus produced by 'length' vibrations (i.e. in the direction of the longest dimension) and higher frequencies by 'thickness' vibrations (i.e. along the shortest dimension). A simple method of exciting a quartz crystal is illustrated in *Figure 3.2*.

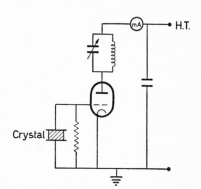

Figure 3.2. Pierce type circuit for exciting a quartz crystal

Maximum acoustic energies are obtained by operating at the fundamental natural frequencies, but for the propagation of high frequencies it may be necessary to use upper harmonics. To generate frequencies of 20 Mc/s an X-cut quartz crystal plate about 0·15 mm thick is necessary for the fundamental 'thickness' mode. Such a plate is extremely brittle and, for too high an applied voltage, it may shatter or perhaps its dielectric properties would break down. For the propagation of ultrasonic waves having frequencies of this and higher orders it is normal to use thicker crystals with lower fundamental frequencies, and to operate at one of the upper harmonics. Bergmann[2] (p. 19) has quoted the example of the generation of waves having a frequency of about 55 Mc/s by vibrating a quartz crystal about 1 cm thick at its 191st harmonic. More recently, Bömmel and Dransfeld[3] have, using electromagnetic cavity resonators, excited vibrations of frequency 10,000 Mc/s in a long quartz crystal under non-resonant conditions.

Because the piezoelectric effect can occur only when opposite charges appear on the electrodes, only odd harmonics can be generated. This can be explained by reference to *Figure 3.3*. When a crystal is excited at its nth harmonic its thickness is divided into n equal parts with compressions and expansions taking place in adjoining sections. Where n is even, compressions occur in $n/2$ of the sections and expansions occur in the remaining sections; thus there is no net strain in the crystal. Where n is odd, however, $(n-1)/2$ compressions neutralize the same number of expansions, leaving either a compression or an expansion in the remaining section

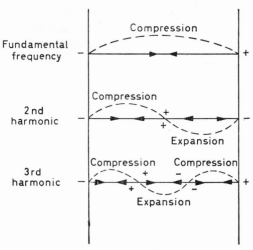

Figure 3.3. Distribution of pressure and charge for a quartz crystal oscillating at the fundamental frequency and at the second and third harmonics (after Bergmann[2])

3.2.2. The Electrostrictive Effect

The electrostrictive effect occurs in all dielectrics and is a phenomenon analogous to magnetostriction (Section 3.8). For most materials it is negligible, but in certain dielectrics, called *ferroelectrics*, the effect is strongly pronounced. The application of an electric field in a given direction produces a mechanical strain, the magnitude of which is proportional to the square of the applied field strength and is thus independent of the sense of the field. Consequently a positive strain may occur for both positive and negative values of the exciting field. For a sinusoidally applied electric field, the wave-form of the strain is the same as that of a rectified but unsmoothed alternating current, and its frequency is equal to twice that of the applied field. To obtain a sinusoidal variation in strain one must polarize the transducer, cf. magneto-strictive transducers. This can be done permanently by heating it to a temperature above the Curie point (i.e. the temperature at which electrostriction disappears) and then allowing it to cool slowly in a strong electric field orientated in the direction in which it is intended to apply the exciting field. Provided that the exciting field is small compared with the initial polarizing field, the strain will vary sinusoidally at the frequency of the exciting field.

A polarized ferroelectric transducer appears to display the same effect as a piezoelectric transducer and, for this reason, it is commonly referred to as being 'piezoelectric'. At present, barium titanate and lead zirconate are the substances most widely used for electro-strictive applications. For the construction of this type of transducer many small crystallites of ferroelectric material together with suit-able additives are bonded together to form a ceramic of the required shape. Because these materials are polycrystalline, they have the advantage over naturally occurring piezoelectric crystals in that they are isotropic and do not have to be cut along specified axes. Thus it is possible to produce a concave transducer with shapes so that ultrasonic radiation can be focussed without the use of an auxiliary lens system.

3.3. PIEZOELECTRIC RELATIONS

Consider a piezoelectric crystal of cross-sectional area, A, and thickness, l, with electrodes plated on its opposite faces. Let a voltage, V, be applied across the electrodes to produce a field, $E = V/l$, and a constant tensile stress, T, be applied to the surfaces. If S is the resultant mechanical strain and, provided that the changes occur within the elastic limit, we have:

$$S = Ts + Ed' \tag{3.1}$$

and
$$D = Td + \epsilon E \tag{3.2}$$

where D is the electric displacement and s, d, d' and t are coefficients which will be defined later. On short-circuiting the electrodes so that $E = 0$, equation 3.1 may be written as:

$$D = Td$$

Here the electric displacement, D, becomes equal to the dielectric polarization, P, i.e. the charge per unit area.

Thus $\qquad P = Td \qquad$ (under short-circuit conditions) (3.3)

d is called the 'd' coefficient or the *piezoelectric strain constant* and is defined as the charge density output per unit applied stress under short-circuit conditions.

If, on the other hand, the stress, T, is removed, equation 3.2 becomes:

$$S = Ed'$$

A consideration of the principle of conservation of energy shows that $d = d'$ and we have

$$S = Ed \qquad \text{(under conditions of no load)} \qquad (3.4)$$

d may thus be defined alternatively as the mechanical strain produced by unit applied field under conditions of no load and is expressed either in coulomb newton^{-1} or metre volt^{-1}. Equation 3.1 then becomes:

$$S = Ts + Ed \qquad (3.5)$$

In the absence of the piezoelectric effect, the term d disappears from equations 3.2 and 3.5 and we have the well-known relationships:

$$S = Ts \qquad (3.6)$$

and: $$D = \epsilon E \qquad (3.7)$$

where s is the elastic constant for the medium and ϵ its electrical permittivity.

Equations 3.3 and 3.6 lead to:

$$P = eS \qquad \text{(under short-circuit conditions)} \qquad (3.8)$$

where: $$e = d/s \qquad (3.9)$$

When the crystal is subjected to a compressive stress, T, equation 3.5 becomes:

$$S = -Ts + Ed \qquad (3.5a)$$

and where the stress is of such a value that the resultant strain is zero, i.e. when the crystal is clamped, it can be seen from equations 3.5a and 3.9 that:

$$T = Ee \qquad \text{(under clamped conditions)} \qquad (3.10)$$

e is called the 'e' coefficient or the *piezoelectric stress constant* and may be expressed either in coulomb m^{-2} or newton volt^{-1} m^{-1}.

In addition, two other constants, the 'g' and 'h' coefficients, are sometimes used to describe the behaviour of piezoelectric crystals. The 'g' coefficient is the electric field produced per unit applied stress and the 'h' coefficient is the electric field produced per unit strain, in both cases under conditions of open circuit. g is expressed in volt-metre newton^{-1} and h in newton coulomb^{-1}.

i.e.: $\qquad\qquad E = gT$ (open-circuit conditions)

$\qquad\qquad\qquad E = hS$ (open-circuit conditions)

for compressions. It may be shown that:

$$g = d/e$$

and $\qquad\qquad\qquad h = g/s$

It has been assumed up to now that the changes in E, T, S, and P have been in the thickness direction of the crystal. In general, one must take into account variations which may occur in any direction. A stress applied to a solid in a given direction may be resolved into six components, three of tensile stress, T_1, T_2 and T_3, along the x, y and z axes respectively and another three of shear stress, T_4, T_5 and T_6, about those axes. The corresponding components of strain are S_1, S_2, S_3, S_4, S_5 and S_6. Thus, in general,

$$S_h = s_{hk}\, T_k \qquad\qquad (3.6a)$$

or, if one considers the elastic modulus or stiffness coefficient, $c_{hk} = 1/s_{hk}$ we have:

$$T_h = c_{hk}\, S_k \qquad\qquad (3.6b)$$

This gives 36 values of c_{hk} as follows:

$$T_1 = c_{11}S_1 + c_{12}S_2 + c_{13}S_3 + c_{14}S_4 + c_{15}S_5 + c_{16}S_6$$
$$T_2 = c_{21}S_1 + c_{22}S_2 + c_{23}S_3 + c_{24}S_4 + c_{25}S_5 + c_{26}S_6$$
$$T_3 = c_{31}S_1 + c_{32}S_2 + c_{33}S_3 + c_{34}S_4 + c_{35}S_5 + c_{36}S_6$$
$$T_4 = c_{41}S_1 + c_{42}S_2 + c_{43}S_3 + c_{44}S_4 + c_{45}S_5 + c_{46}S_6 \qquad (3.11)$$
$$T_5 = c_{51}S_1 + c_{52}S_2 + c_{53}S_3 + c_{54}S_4 + c_{55}S_5 + c_{56}S_6$$
$$T_6 = c_{61}S_1 + c_{62}S_2 + c_{63}S_3 + c_{64}S_4 + c_{65}S_5 + c_{66}S_6$$

Equation 3.6b may be expanded in a similar manner, thus yielding 36 values of s_{hk}.

From the principle of conservation of energy it can be seen that:

$$c_{hk} = c_{kh} \text{ and } s_{hk} = s_{kh}$$

so that the number of these constants is reduced to 21. Symmetry of axes will reduce this number still further. With quartz, for example, we find that only six elastic constants are independent of one another. Values of c_{hk} may be expressed in the following matrix form:

$$
\begin{vmatrix}
c_{11} & c_{12} & c_{13} & c_{14} & 0 & 0 \\
c_{12} & c_{11} & c_{13} & -c_{14} & 0 & 0 \\
c_{13} & c_{13} & c_{33} & 0 & 0 & 0 \\
c_{14} & -c_{14} & 0 & c_{44} & 0 & 0 \\
0 & 0 & 0 & 0 & c_{44} & c_{14} \\
0 & 0 & 0 & 0 & c_{14} & (c_{11}-c_{12})/2
\end{vmatrix}
$$

For quartz, values of these constants for adiabatic conditions, as given by Cady[4], are listed in *Table 3.1*.

Table 3.1. Accepted Values of the Adiabatic Elastic Constants of Quartz (after Cady[4])

$\times 10^{-12}$ cm^2 dyne^{-1} or $\times 10^{-11}$ m^2 newton^{-1}	$\times 10^{10}$ dyne cm^{-2} or $\times 10^{9}$ newton m^{-2}
$s_{11} = 1 \cdot 26(9)$	$c_{11} = 87 \cdot (5)$
$s_{33} = 0 \cdot 97(1)$	$c_{33} = 107 \cdot (7)$
$s_{44} = 2 \cdot 00(5)$	$c_{44} = 57 \cdot (3)$
$s_{12} = -0 \cdot 16(9)$	$c_{12} = 7 \cdot 6(2)$
$s_{13} = -0 \cdot 15(4)$	$c_{13} = 15 \cdot (1)$
$s_{14} = -0 \cdot 43(1)$	$c_{14} = 17 \cdot (2)$

For both E and P there are three components. Equations 3.3, 3.4, 3.8, and 3.10 are expressed in the general form as follows:

$$P_r = T_h d_{ih} \tag{3.3a}$$

$$S_h = E_i d_{ih} \tag{3.4a}$$

$$P_i = S_h e_{ih} \tag{3.8a}$$

$$T_h = E_i e_{ih} \tag{3.10a}$$

so that:
$$e_{ik} = \sum_h c_{kh} d_{ih} \tag{3.12}$$

Values of h and k, respectively, run from 1 to 6 and values of i from 1 to 3. There are 18 values each for d and e. Values of d are expressed as follows:

$$\text{for compressions: } \begin{aligned} S_1 &= d_{11}E_1 + d_{21}E_2 + d_{31}E_3 \\ S_2 &= d_{12}E_1 + d_{22}E_2 + d_{32}E_3 \\ S_3 &= d_{13}E_1 + d_{23}E_2 + d_{33}E_3 \end{aligned}$$

$$\text{and for shears: } \begin{aligned} S_4 &= d_{14}E_1 + d_{24}E_2 + d_{34}E_3 \\ S_5 &= d_{15}E_1 + d_{25}E_2 + d_{35}E_3 \\ S_6 &= d_{16}E_1 + d_{26}E_2 + d_{36}E_3 \end{aligned} \tag{3.13}$$

The number of d terms is reduced because of symmetry and the fact that there would be no piezoelectric effect along the axes of symmetry. For quartz all values of d except d_{11}, d_{12}, d_{14}, d_{25} and d_{26} are zero and, for symmetry,

$$d_{12} = -d_{11}, \quad d_{25} = -d_{14} \text{ and } d_{26} = 2d_{11}$$

48

so that equations 3.13 are reduced to:

$$S_1 = d_{11}E_1 \qquad\qquad S_5 = -d_{14}E_2$$
$$S_2 = -d_{11}E_1 \qquad\qquad S_6 = -2d_{11}E_2 \qquad\qquad (3.14)$$
$$S_4 = d_{14}E_1$$

For quartz we have $d_{11} = -2 \cdot 3 \times 10^{12}$ coulombs newton^{-1} and $d_{14} = 0 \cdot 57 \times 10^{12}$ coulombs newton^{-1}. Values of d for a number of piezoelectric materials are given in *Table 3.2*.

Table 3.2. Principal Piezoelectric Properties of some of the More Common Transducer Materials

Substance	Dielectric constant*	d coulomb newton^{-1} $\times 10^{-12}$	k_c %	Upper Curie Temp. °C
Quartz (X-cut)	4·5	2·3	11	550
Barium titanate	400 to 1700	60 to 190	20 to 50	120 to 140
Lead zirconate titanate	900 to 1500	80 to 320	23 to 76	350 to 490
Rochelle salt (45° Y-cut)	9·4	27	29	45
Rochelle salt (45° X-cut)	450	430	78	45
ADP (45° Z-cut)	15	24	29	120

The values quoted above, which hold for thickness vibrations, are approximate and apply to room temperatures. They are based on information supplied by Hueter and Bolt [6] and Crawford.[7]

* The value of ϵ is obtained by multiplying this quantity by $(1/36\pi) \times 10^{-9}$ farad m^{-1}.

Equations 3.2 and 3.5 may now be expressed in the general form as follows:

$$D_i = T_h d_{ih} + \epsilon_{ij}E_j \qquad\qquad (3.2a)$$

$$S_h = T_k s_{hk} + E_i d_{ih} \qquad\qquad (3.5a)$$

If T is eliminated from equations 3.2 and 3.5 we have:

$$D = Sd/s + \epsilon E(1 - d^2/\epsilon s) \qquad (3.18)$$

i.e. $\qquad\qquad D = Se + \epsilon E(1 - k_c^2) \qquad (3.18a)$

where k_c is termed the *electro-mechanical coupling factor* and is expressed by the relationship:

$$k_c^2 = d^2/\epsilon s = e^2 s/\epsilon \qquad (3.19)$$

The significance of k_c is explained later but it can be seen that for a clamped transducer, i.e. S being made to equal zero in equation 3.18a, k_c^2 is the fractional decrease in electrical permittivity of the crystal due to the piezoelectric effect.

3.4. DYNAMIC CHARACTERISTICS OF PIEZOELECTRIC TRANSDUCERS

3.4.1. General Considerations

It has been shown in Section 2.2.3 that the behaviour of a body undergoing forced vibrations is analogous to an electrical circuit which is excited by an alternating E.M.F., the velocity, u, corresponding to the current, i, and the applied force, F, to the voltage, V.

Now, $u = l\mathrm{d}S/\mathrm{d}t$ and current, $i = \mathrm{d}Q/\mathrm{d}t = A\mathrm{d}P/\mathrm{d}t$

From equation 3.8 we have: $\mathrm{d}P/\mathrm{d}t = e\mathrm{d}S/\mathrm{d}t$

so that $\qquad\qquad i = (Ae/l)\, u = a_T u \qquad (3.20)$

where $a_T = Ae/l$.

a_T is termed the *transformation factor*, which is constant for a particular transducer. Because P has 3 components and S has 6 components, i and u will have, respectively, 3 and 6 components each and equation 3.20 may be expressed in the general form as:

$$i_i = a_{ih} u_h \qquad (3.20a)$$

From equation 3.10, $\qquad F = (Ae/l)V = a_T V \qquad (3.21)$

or, $\qquad\qquad F_h = a_{hi} V_i \qquad (3.21a)$

The mechanical compliance, C_m, is equivalent to an electrical capacitance, C. Here:

$$C_m = Sl/F = Sl/TA = sl/A \qquad (3.22)$$

The mechanical energy, W_m stored in the transducer when an applied force, F, produces a strain, S, is given by the expression:

$$W_m = \tfrac{1}{2}FSl = \tfrac{1}{2}F^2 C_m = \tfrac{1}{2}a_T^2 V^2 C_m = \tfrac{1}{2}V^2 C$$

where $\qquad\qquad C = a_T^2 C_m \qquad (3.23)$

50

Now, the electrical capacitance, C_0, between the electrodes of the transducer is expressed by the relationship:

$$C_0 = \epsilon A / l \qquad (3.24)$$

The electrical energy, W_e, supplied to the transducer is given by

$$W_e = \tfrac{1}{2} V^2 C_0$$

hence, from equations, 3.20, 3.23 and 3.24, it is seen that the ratio of mechanical energy stored in a piezoelectric transducer to the electrical energy supplied to it is given by:

$$W_m / W_e = C/C_0 = a_T{}^2 C_m / C_0 = e^2 s / \epsilon = k_c{}^2 \text{ (from 3.19)}$$
$$(3.25)$$

Hence the electro-mechanical coupling factor, k_c, is a measure of the efficiency of the transducer.

3.4.2. *Equivalent Electrical Circuit of a Transducer*

Let a parallel-faced transducer be mounted so as to execute piston-like vibrations. Provided that the diameter of the radiating surface contains a sufficiently large number of wavelengths, plane waves are propagated when a periodic force, $F = F_0 \sin \omega t$, is applied. For vibrations in the x direction the equation of motion is given by equation 2.10, i.e.:

$$M \mathrm{d}^2 x / \mathrm{d}t^2 + R_m \mathrm{d}x / \mathrm{d}t + x / C_m = F \qquad (3.26)$$

The mechanical resistance, R_m, has two components due to:

(i) the loading of the transducer by the medium in contact with it, and

(ii) energy losses characteristic of the method of mounting the transducer.

We shall assume for the sake of simplicity that the mounting is frictionless so that only radiation losses need be considered. Because plane waves are propagated, the specific acoustic impedance, Z_a, of the medium is entirely real and thus equal to ρc, the characteristic impedance. At the radiating surface of the transducer, the acoustic pressure and particle velocity have the same respective values as the stress, T, and the velocity, u for the transducer surface.

Hence, $$R_m = TA/u = \rho c A \qquad (3.27)$$

For steady state conditions the solution of equation 3.26 is:

$$\begin{aligned} u = \mathrm{d}x/\mathrm{d}t &= F/\{R_m + j(\omega M - 1/\omega C_m)\} \\ &= F/Z_m = a_T V/Z_m \end{aligned} \qquad (3.28)$$

where Z_m is the mechanical impedance of the transducer.

Putting Z as the electrical impedance equivalent to Z_m we have

$$Z = V/i = V/a_T u \qquad (3.29)$$

Thus, from equations 3.28 and 3.29 we obtain

$$Z = Z_m/a_T{}^2 C_m \qquad (3.30)$$

Thus, the equivalent values for electrical resistance, R, electrical inductance, L, and electrical capacitance, C, are $R_m/a_T{}^2$, $M/a_T{}^2$ and $a_T{}^2/C_m$. The capacitance equivalent has already been given in equation 3.23, obtained from considerations of energy. The equivalent electrical circuit of the transducer thus consists of a resistance,

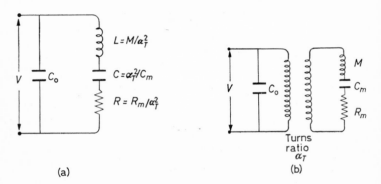

(a)

(b)

Figure 3.4. Equivalent electrical circuits for a transducer

R, an inductance, L, and a capacitance, C, in series, together with the electrical capacitance, C_0, between the electrodes, shunted across this arrangement (see *Figure 3.4a*). Alternatively, one may, from the relationship, $F = a_T V$, employ the circuit of *Figure 3.4b*, where the turns ratio of the transformer is equal to a_T.

For most applications to ultrasonic propagation, transducers are operated under resonance conditions for which $R_m = Z_m$, and the fundamental natural frequency, $f_r = \omega_r/2\pi$, of the crystal is given by equation 2.1, i.e.:

$$\omega_r = 1/(MC_m)^{\frac{1}{2}} = 1/(LC)^{\frac{1}{2}} \qquad (3.31)$$

If one face is kept rigid and the other left free to vibrate we have conditions for *quarter-wavelength resonance* for which the thickness, l, of the crystal is equal to $\lambda'/4$, where λ' is the wavelength of sound in the material of the transducer. Because of variations of strain throughout the crystal, the value of C_m in equation 3.22, as obtained from statical considerations, is no longer valid and a 'motional' compliance, C_m, must be used. Substituting $1/s$ for E in equation 2.26, the velocity of sound in the transducer is given by the expression:

$$c' = 1/(s\rho')^{\frac{1}{2}} \qquad (3.32)$$

so that:

$$f_r = c'/\lambda' = 1/4l \ (s\rho')^{\frac{1}{2}} = 1/2\pi(MC_m)^{\frac{1}{2}} \qquad (3.33)$$

Here ρ' and c' represent the density and acoustic velocity, respectively, for the material of the transducer. Combining equations 3.31 and 3.33 and remembering that $M = \rho'Al$, we find that:

$$C_m' = 4sl/\pi^2A = 4C_m/\pi^2 \ \text{(quarter-wave)} \qquad (3.34a)$$

Quarter-wavelength resonance may be achieved in practice by backing the transducer with an identical crystal having its free surface radiating into the same medium. The boundary between the two crystals forms a nodal plane. This is, in effect, a crystal vibrating at *half-wavelength resonance* into a symmetrical load. Alternatively, the transducer, if radiating into a medium other than a gas, may be backed by a similar one with its radiating face in contact with a medium of negligible characteristic impedance, such as air, i.e. we have an air-backed half-wavelength crystal.

With both arrangements for half-wavelength resonance just described, the effective crystal thickness is reduced by half and the 'motional' compliance is now:

$$C_m' = 2sl/\pi^2A = 2C_m/\pi^2 \qquad \text{(half-wave)} \qquad (3.34b)$$

and the effective mass $M' = \frac{1}{2}l\rho'A = M/2$ (half-wave) (3.35)

In addition, the voltage, V, is halved.

The velocity of the free ends of a transducer radiating into a symmetrical load, as expressed by equation 3.28, is given by:

$$u = a_T V/2R_m = a_T V/2\rho cA \ \text{(symmetrical load)} \qquad (3.36)$$

For the air-backed transducer, however, almost total reflection takes place at the surface in contact with air (see Section 2.11.1) and the reflected waves arrive at the opposite surface in phase with the waves generated by the latter. This results in a doubling of the velocity of the radiating surface.

Thus,

$$u = 2a_T V/2R_m = a_T V/\rho cA \ \text{(air-backing)} \qquad (3.37)$$

A transducer, when mounted symmetrically in a fluid having a low characteristic impedance, can be made effectively 'air-backed' by an arrangement known as *quarter-wavelength backing*. If a solid reflector be placed parallel with the rear surface of the crystal and at a distance from it of exactly a quarter-wavelength, it can be seen from equation 2.61a that the amount of energy reflected is very high. For gases it approaches 100 per cent and for light liquids such as water, it is of the order of 95 per cent.

3.4.3. 'Q' of a Transducer

The Q factor of a system, either electrical or mechanical, determines the frequency response of that system, i.e. for a low Q the frequency bandwidth is wide, whereas for a high Q it is narrow (see Section 2.2.4). A transducer has two Q factors, one mechanical, expressed as Q_m and the other electrical, represented simply by Q. Now, Q_m is defined as

$$Q_m = \omega M / R_m \qquad (3.38)$$

Modifying equation 3.33 for half-wavelength resonance we have

$$\omega_r = \pi / l (\rho' s')^{\frac{1}{2}} = \pi c' l = 2\pi c' \lambda'$$

where c' and λ' are the respective velocity and wavelength for the transducer material. Thus, we have:

$$Q_m = \frac{\pi}{2} \frac{\rho' c'}{\rho c} \qquad (3.39)$$

Equation 3.39 represents the ideal case for which only the damping by the load is considered. It ignores the friction due to the mounting of the crystal and also any internal friction in the transducer itself. For many crystals, such as quartz, the latter consideration is negligible under normal conditions but for other transducer materials, including barium titanate, internal friction may be very high. For example, under identical conditions of mounting the value of Q_m for quartz in atmospheric air may be about 10,000, whereas that for barium titanate would be only 200. The mechanism for internal damping in ferroelectric materials is discussed in Section 6.5.

For the electrical Q factor the capacitance, C_0, between the electrodes must be taken into account. At resonance frequencies, however, the only effective mechanical impedance of the crystal is R_m. Hence,

$$Q \simeq \omega_r C_0 R = \omega_r C_0 R_m / a_T{}^2$$

which, by substitution of equations 3.20, 3.24 and 3.27, gives

$$Q \simeq (\pi \epsilon e^2 s) \frac{\rho c}{\rho' c'} = \frac{\pi}{k_c{}^2} \frac{\rho c}{\rho' c'} \qquad (3.39)$$

i.e.
$$Q \simeq \frac{\pi^2}{2k_c{}^2} \Big/ Q_m \qquad (3.40)$$

3.4.4. Impedance Matching

Only part of the current supplied to a crystal transducer is used to maintain its vibrations. The remainder is short-circuited through the capacitance, C_0, in parallel with the effective transducer circuit. This may be prevented by connecting a coil of inductance, L_0, across the crystal to tune out C_0. The value of L_0 is chosen such that:

$$\omega = 1/(L_0 C_0)^{\frac{1}{2}}$$

Maximum efficiency is obtained by matching the impedance, R', of the current source to the impedance, R_1, of the transducer by means of a transformer. The number of turns, n', of the primary winding is chosen to give the ratio, $n'^2/n^2 = R'/R_1$, where n is the

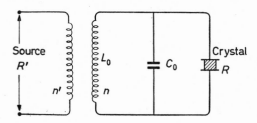

Figure 3.5. Transformer used for matching electrical source with transducer

number of turns of the secondary coil, L_0 (see *Figure 3.5*). The effective impedance, R_1, of the crystal is then given by:

$$R_1 = R/(R^2\omega^2 C_0{}^2 + 1) \tag{3.41}$$

In estimating the efficiency of a transducer, account must be taken of losses in the exciting circuit, losses due to mounting, and dielectric losses. For a well-matched and properly mounted transducer, Hueter and Bolt[5] (p. 122) have shown that this is about 60 per cent for quartz and about 30 per cent for barium titanate at a frequency of 1 Mc/s, when using an amplifier under class C conditions.

3.5. PROPERTIES OF PIEZOELECTRIC CRYSTALS

The piezoelectric effect is displayed by a large number of crystals and much has been written about their properties (see, for example Cady[4], Mason[6] and Crawford[7]) but, because of their unsuitable physical or chemical characteristics, only a small number are of any practical use for the propagation of ultrasonic waves. Vigoureux and

Booth[1] have listed the following requirements for the material of an ultrasonic transducer:

(i) it should have satisfactory piezoelectric characteristics for the required modes of vibration,

(ii) it should be homogeneous throughout,

(iii) it must be capable of being worked to the desired shape and size,

(iv) variations of its properties with temperature should be small,

(v) its internal friction should be as low as possible,

(vi) it should be both chemically and physically stable, and

(vii) it must retain its piezoelectric properties over the complete range of temperature for which it is to be used.

In addition to the above requirements it is desirable, for maximum efficiency, that the transducer should be capable of satisfactory matching with both the electrical circuit and the medium of propagation. Furthermore, especially for analytical applications, steps must be taken to avoid the generation of parasitic frequencies, which may arise from an unsatisfactory mounting or from frequency coupling between different modes of vibration. Thus when a crystal is excited at its fundamental thickness mode, a harmonic of one of its other modes having a frequency very close to the fundamental can also be generated. Bechmann[8] has shown that this difficulty may be overcome by bevelling the edges of the transducer.

For many ultrasonic applications quartz possesses most or all of the desirable properties of a transducer, especially for the measurement of propagation constants at megacycle frequencies. It can be used under widely varying physical conditions. Quartz has a Curie temperature of $573°$ C and is very stable both chemically and physically, except at high temperatures and pressures where it becomes partially soluble in water. It has a low temperature coefficient of frequency and for certain cuts this coefficient is practically zero. Internal losses are very small; if properly mounted in air quartz has a Q factor of about 25,000. It is easily worked and very thin specimens, as little as 0.1 mm thick, may be cut. Because of its high electrical impedance and low piezoelectric constants, it does not normally provide a satisfactory source for high power radiation. Quartz is now becoming available in decreasing quantities and is thus expensive. Less expensive substitutes such as Rochelle salt, lithium sulphate and a number of artificially grown crystals, including ammonium dihydrogen phosphate (ADP), potassium dihydrogen phosphate (KDP), ethylene diamine tartrate (EDT), and dipotassium tartrate (DKT), are now available.

Rochelle salt is strongly piezoelectric but it is very susceptible to the amount of moisture in the surrounding atmosphere. It dehydrates when the relative humidity is less than 35 per cent, and slowly dissolves for an atmospheric moisture content of more than 85 per cent. Disintegration occurs at a temperature of 55° C. ADP and, to a lesser extent, KDP have high piezoelectric coefficients but, although they do not dehydrate at low humidities, they dissolve in atmospheres with relative humidities greater than 95 per cent; they disintegrate at temperatures in the region of 100° C. EDP and DKT have high mechanical Q factors but they also deliquesce at high humidities. The crystals mentioned in this paragraph are used mainly as audio-frequency transducers and filters, but Rochelle salt, lithium sulphate, and ADP are sometimes used for ultrasonics.

For pulse techniques and for high-power applications, where the requirements include low impedances and high piezoelectric constants, but where frequency stability is not essential, ceramic transducers such as barium titanate, lead zirconate-titanate, and lead meta-niobate are now in common use. The properties of these ceramics can be adjusted by means of additives in varying amounts. Barium titanate ceramics have low Curie temperatures but lead zirconate-titanate ceramics have recently been developed to yield Curie temperatures of up to 490° C[9]. Pure lead zirconate ($PbZrO_3$) is a non-ferroelectric but if mixed with more than 10 mole per cent lead titanate ($PbTiO_3$) it acquires ferroelectric properties. A high Curie temperature is important for processing work for which heating of the transducer will occur.

3.6. THE PREPARATION AND MOUNTING OF CRYSTAL SOURCES

3.6.1. General Considerations

A crystal transducer must be provided with electrodes before it can be used for ultrasonic propagation. The electrodes should be as light as possible, so as not to affect the vibrational characteristics of the transducer, and they should also be durable. In most cases a thin film of some metal such as aluminium, silver, or gold, plated on to the crystal surfaces either by an electrolytic method or by cathode sputtering would suffice, but for high-power applications more substantial electrodes of metal foil or plate may be required.

For single crystal transducers, which are naturally piezoelectric, the plate should be cut perpendicular to the axis suitable for the desired mode of vibration. Mason[6] has described the various ways in which a crystal can be cut. For quartz, X-cut plates are used for the generation of compressional waves and Y-cut plates for the propagation of shear waves. Where low temperature coefficients of frequency are required for shear waves, AC or AT cut plates may be used. These are Y-cuts which are rotated by $32°$ and $38°$ $15'$, respectively, in a positive direction about the X-axis.

Where a polycrystalline ceramic transducer is used for longitudinal wave propagation, the initial polarization lies in the same direction as that of the applied alternating field. When it is polarized in a direction at right-angles to that of the exciting field, a ceramic transducer will generate shear waves, although at the same time it will also be vibrating longitudinally with small amplitude at a frequency double that of the shear waves.

A crystal transducer must have a suitable mechanical support and be provided with a good electrical contact with the electrodes. The method of mounting will depend on the type of application and a number of different types of crystal holders have been designed accordingly. Some of these are described in the sections dealing with these applications.

With gases there is an extremely poor degree of coupling between the source and medium, and, for efficiency of transfer, the crystal should be mounted for minimum damping. Two such methods of mounting quartz crystals for interferometer applications are described in Section 4.11.3. The more efficient of these is the nodal type of mounting but where it is used at high frequencies, for which the crystal thickness should be small, extreme accuracy is called for in locating the nodal plane. The other method of mounting, although less efficient, is more practicable. The transducer is lightly clamped to a metal backing surface. The clamping should be sufficient to ensure good electrical contact but should not impede the vibrations by any appreciable amount. Energy transfer efficiency is improved further by quarter-wavelength backing (see Sections 2.11.2 and 4.10.3).

For the radiation of ultrasonic waves into liquids and solids the mounting of the crystal presents less of a problem, because of the more efficient coupling. For pulse techniques and where the transducer is used under off-resonance conditions, the crystal holder must be designed for high damping (see Sections 6.11 and 6.12).

With conducting liquids, precautions must be taken for no current to flow between the electrodes via the fluid, and it is common to mount the crystal in an insulating liquid and couple it to the liquid under test by means of a ρc rubber membrane (see Section 5.7). High power propagation in fluid is limited by the following considerations:

(a) the voltage across the electrodes may be high enough for the dielectric properties of the liquid to break down;

(b) the crystal may be heated to a temperature above its Curie point, and

(c) the energy of vibrations may be sufficient to cause the crystal to fracture.

The first difficulty can be overcome by the use of a transducer, such as one of the ceramics, having a high electromechanical coupling coefficient, k_c. Where, however, it is necessary to use a quartz crystal source, i.e. where a narrow frequency band is required, the transducer must be mounted in a liquid having a very high dielectric strength. Overheating may be reduced by pulsing the sound waves or by the use of a suitable cooling system. Fracturing of the crystal presents no problem for liquids, because the amount of energy necessary for this to happen is usually much less than the amount which would give rise to dielectric breakdown or overheating. This trouble, however, does arise for gases because of the poorer coupling involved.

3.6.2. Mosaics

Where it is required to irradiate over a large area of cross-section and transducers having sufficiently large surface areas are not available, one can use a mosaic of crystals. This is a number of similar crystal elements mounted side by side. Anan'eva[10] describes a mosaic consisting of 21 barium titanate plates, each having dimensions $20 \times 20 \times 5$ mm, mounted on a steel surface. Mosaics mounted on concave surfaces are used as focussing devices.

3.6.3. Sandwich Transducers

The generation of resonant thickness modes at low frequencies from quartz crystals is an expensive operation because of the greater thickness of crystal required. This operation becomes difficult owing to the high electrical impedance of the transducer. In 1921, Langevin, using a sandwich arrangement, showed that a quartz crystal could resonate at a frequency much lower than that characterized by its thickness. An arrangement may consist of a thin quartz crystal and two thicker steel plates cemented to each side. Where the front layer is made one quarter-wavelength thick and t_q and t_b are the respective thicknesses of the quartz and back plate, we have:

$$\tan(2\pi t_q/\lambda_q) . \tan(2\pi t_b/\lambda_b) = \rho_q c_q / \rho_b c_b.$$

This would give a maximum output at the required frequency. Langevin constructed a 40 kc/s generator with the front plate 3 cm thick, the back plate 0·6 cm thick, and the quartz crystal also 0·6 cm thick.

Hatfield[11] described a multiple sandwich transducer consisting of four similar X-cut quartz crystals interspersed alternately with five steel slabs; this was designed to operate at a fundamental frequency of 50 kc/s. Such an arrangement gives a much higher acoustic output than would be obtained if only a single sandwich were used.

A fuller description of sandwich transducers has been given by Hueter and Bolt[5] (p. 136).

3.7. CRYSTAL RECEIVERS

3.7.1. General Considerations

Piezoelectric crystals, when used as receivers, are employed in both categories (a) and (b) as listed in Section 3.1. Because they are reversible in operation, crystal receivers of class A may be identical in design to crystal generators and, where echo techniques are used, such as for the interferometer and the pulse method, one crystal may serve as both sender and receiver.

For class (b) types of receiver, i.e. probes, the basic requirement is that the dimensions of the microphone should be small compared with wavelength. This does not present much difficulty where unidirectional sound fields in liquids are to be investigated. It is common practice for the transducer to be operated below its fundamental resonance frequency.

The author has used a method in which a tapered metal rod coupled to a transducer element was immersed in the sound field with the waves incident normally to the end surface (see *Figure 3.6*). This method had three advantages:

(a) the transducer element itself was not immersed in the liquid.

(b) the dimensions of the free end surface of the rod could be made small compared with wavelength, and

(c) the rod acted as an acoustic transformer (see Section 3.12). Greater sensitivity was obtained by designing the coupling rod so that it resonated at the frequency of the sound waves.

Relative intensity measurements were made in water in which stationary waves were generated at a frequency of 40 kc/s. The transducer was a U.I.C. barium titanate accelerometer connected directly to a valve-voltmeter, via a coaxial cable. R.M.S. readings of 3 volts were observed when the liquid was excited to just above the cavitation threshold (see Section 8.2).

Much work has been done on the design of non-directional microphones which, ideally, should be spherical in shape. A description of these has been given by Anan'eva.[12] In most cases the problems are two dimensional, and cylindrical transducers usually suffice. Because of their ease of shaping and of their greater piezoelectric strengths, ceramic transducers are normally used.

Cylindrical transducers in the forms of tubes can vibrate in three different modes, i.e. length, radial, and wall-thickness. Fundamental frequencies for length and radial modes are comparatively low whereas that for the wall-thickness mode is high for a thin-walled cylindrical tube. Coupling may thus be expected to occur between the various natural frequencies of the length and radial modes. A

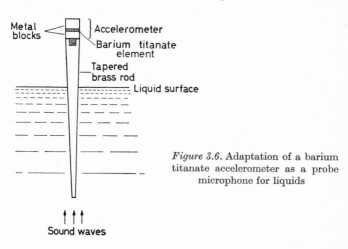

Figure 3.6. Adaptation of a barium titanate accelerometer as a probe microphone for liquids

barium titanate cylindrical probe designed by Schilling and his colleagues (see Hueter and Bolt[5], p. 151) has an outside diameter of 1/16 inch, a length of 1/16 inch and a wall-diameter of 0·012 inch.

3.7.2. *The Sensitivity of Piezoelectric Microphones*

Where, as for most piezoelectric probes, the receiving transducer is operated below resonance, its mechanical reactance, X_m (see equation 2.14) is given by:

$$X_m = \omega M - 1/\omega C_m \simeq -1/\omega C_m$$

where
$$\omega \ll \omega_r = 1/(MC_m)^{\frac{1}{2}}$$

Furthermore, where the mechanical resistance, R_m, due entirely to mounting is low we have:

$$Z_m = R_m + jX_m \simeq 1/j\omega C_m$$

The electrical impedance, Z, of the transducer is that due to the capacitance, C_0, between the electrodes and is given by:

$$Z = 1/j\omega C_0$$

and the corresponding mechanical impedance is $a_T{}^2 Z$ (see equation 3.30).

Thus, the effective mechanical impedance Z_m' of the transducer which terminates the acoustic line is given by:

$$Z_m' = Z_m + a_T{}^2 Z$$

The relationship between the force, F, and the velocity, u, for the transducer is then:

$$F/u = Z_m + a_T{}^2 Z \tag{3.42}$$

Now the open-circuit voltage, V, appearing across the electrodes is equivalent to a force $a_T V$ which is related to the velocity by the expression:

$$V + u a_T{}^2 Z$$

so that equation 3.42 becomes:

$$V = F a_T{}^2 Z / (Z_m + a_T{}^2 Z) \tag{3.43}$$

i.e.: $$a_T V/F = a_T{}^2 C_m / (C_0 + a_T{}^2 C_m)$$

But, from equation 3.25, the electro-mechanical coupling factor, k_c, is given by:

$$k_c{}^2 = a_T{}^2 C_m / C_0$$

Hence, $$V/F = k_c{}^2 / a_T (1 + k_c{}^2) \tag{3.44}$$

The ratio V/F represents the *open circuit sensitivity* of the microphone.

3.8. MAGNETOSTRICTIVE OSCILLATORS

Magnetostriction occurs with ferromagnetic materials and certain non-metals called ferrites. The magnetostrictive effect was discovered by Joule in 1847 and the converse effect by Villari in 1868. When a rod or bar of ferromagnetic or ferrimagnetic material is subjected to a magnetic field it experiences a change in length. Conversely, a mechanical stress applied to a rod or bar causes a change in intensity of magnetization.

The magnetostrictive effect, which is analagous to the electrostrictive effect (Section 3.2.2), is prominent for materials such as nickel, iron and cobalt. Whether there is an increase or decrease in length depends entirely on the nature of the material and on the strength of the applied magnetic field, and this is independent of the direction of the field. *Figure 3.7a* shows how the magnitude of strain varies with changes in value of the applied field, and *Figure 3.7b* illustrates the variation of strain with magnetic polarization. In general, this effect decreases with rise in temperature and disappears at the Curie temperature.

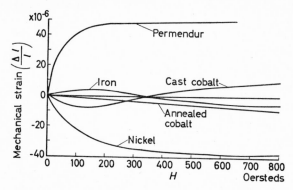

Figure 3.7a. Relationship between mechanical strain and applied magnetic field due to magnetostriction (after Carlin[27])

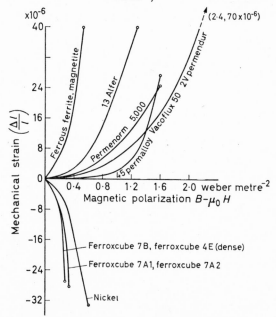

Figure 3.7b. Relationship between mechanical strain and magnetic polarization (after van der Burgt[28])

When an alternating magnetic field is applied along the direction of the axis of a rod of ferromagnetic material, the rod oscillates at twice the frequency of the applied field. For nickel a decrease in length occurs when a field is applied, irrespective of the sense of the field, i.e. a negative strain occurs every half-cycle. The wave-form of the strain is a rectified sine curve so that unwanted harmonics are generated. A purely sinusoidal wave-form, having the frequency of the applied field and accompanied by a greatly increased energy output, is obtained if the rod is polarized. This is done by applying at

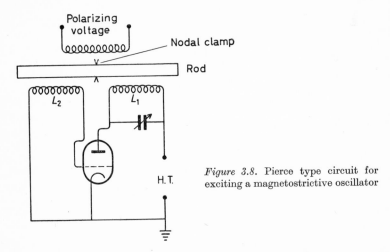

Figure 3.8. Pierce type circuit for exciting a magnetostrictive oscillator

the same time a direct magnetic field of sufficiently high intensity for the value of the magnetic field to remain above zero.

Maximum output is obtained by operating at the fundamental resonant frequency, f_r, of the rod, as given by the expression:

$$f_r = (1/2l) \ (Y_s/\rho)^{\frac{1}{2}} \tag{3.45}$$

where Y_s is the adiabatic Young's modulus for the material of the rod, ρ its density and l its length. At this frequency the mechanical strain is of the order of 10^{-4} compared with 10^{-6} when operating at a non-resonant frequency. *Figure 3.8* shows a simple but effective arrangement for the production of magnetostrictive oscillations.

3.9. STATIC CHARACTERISTICS OF MAGNETOSTRICTIVE TRANSDUCERS

The theory of magnetostrictive oscillators is analogous to that of piezoelectric vibrators, provided that account is taken of the polarizing field, H_0. Consider a ferromagnetic rod polarized along its length with a magnetic field, H_0, and let B_0 represent the corresponding flux density. Because the sign of the resultant strain is independent of the direction of the field, one may assume a square-law relation between the strain S_0 and B_0.

Thus, $$S_0 = CB_0{}^2 \qquad (3.46)$$

where C is a constant.

Let H and B represent the respective values of the exciting field strength and the corresponding flux-density, where H is considerably less than H_0.

i.e.: $$B = \mu_i H = \Delta B_0 \ll B_0$$

where μ_i is the incremental magnetic permeability. Assuming that the rod is kept under constant stress we have, for the resultant strain:

$$S = \Delta S_0$$
$$\Delta S = 2CB_0 \Delta B_0$$

i.e.: $$S = 2CB_0 B = \beta \mu_i H \qquad (3.47)$$

where $\beta = 2CB_0$ is defined as the *magnetostrictive strain coefficient* (in m² weber⁻¹) for small strains. Equation 3.47 is analogous to equation 3.4 for no-load conditions.

Where no alternating field is applied, the value of S is given by Hooke's law, viz.:

$$S = T/Y$$

Thus, one can obtain an expression in the same form as equation 3.48 by putting H in place of E, Y instead of $1/s$, and $\beta \mu_i$ instead of d' or d.

i.e.: $$S = T/Y + \beta \mu_i H \qquad (3.49)$$

for a rod subjected simultaneously to a tensile stress, T, and a magnetic field, H. This analogy may be extended to equation 3.2

to give: $$B = T\beta \mu_i + \mu_i H \qquad (3.50)$$

For a clamped rod, by substituting $S = 0$ in equation 3.48, an expression similar to equation 3.10 is obtained, viz.:

$$T = Y\beta \mu_i H = \Lambda B \qquad (3.51)$$

where T is a compressive stress and $\Lambda = Y\beta$ is defined as the *magnetostrictive stress constant*, measured in newtons weber⁻¹. Mason[13] uses what he calls the *piezomagnetic constant*, characterized by the symbol d, such that $d = 1/\Lambda$ webers newton⁻¹. *Table 3.3* gives the analogies of magnetostrictive with piezoelectric coefficients. From these one can obtain an expression for the electromechanical coupling factor, k_c, similar to equation 3.19, i.e.:

$$k_c{}^2 = \beta^2 \mu_i Y = \Lambda^2 \mu_i / Y = 4 C^2 B^2{}_0 \mu_i Y \qquad (3.52)$$

Since μ_i varies with H for ferromagnetic materials, the values of the coefficients β, Λ and, hence, k_c, depend upon the operating point on the magnetization curve.

Table 3.3. Analogies of Piezoelectric with Magnetostrictive Coefficients

Piezoelectric coefficient	D	E	ϵ	d	s	e	$k_c^2 = d^2/\epsilon s$
Magnetostrictive coefficient	B	H	μ_i	$\beta\mu_i$	$1/Y$	$\Lambda\mu$	$k_c^2 = \beta^2 \mu_i Y$

Table 3.4 lists values of the magnetostrictive coefficients for a number of materials.

Table 3.4. Magnetostrictive Constants for some Transducer Materials

Material	Λ newton weber^{-1}	μ_i henry metre^{-1}	Y newton metre^{-2}	k_c %	Curie temperature °C
Metals Annealed nickel	$-2\cdot0 \times 10^7$	$4\cdot3 \times 10^{-6}$	$2\cdot0 \times 10^{11}$	31	358
Permalloy	$2\cdot7 \times 10^6$	$2\cdot9 \times 10^{-4}$	$1\cdot4 \times 10^{11}$	12	440
Alfer	$6\cdot7 \times 10^6$	$2\cdot4 \times 10^{-4}$	$1\cdot5 \times 10^{11}$	27	500
Ferrites Ferroxcube 4 A	$-9\cdot0 \times 10^7$	$1\cdot9 \times 10^{-2}$	$1\cdot8 \times 10^{11}$	3	190
Ferroxcube 7 A1	$-2\cdot8$ to $4\cdot4$ $\times 10^7$	4–5×10^{-5}	$1\cdot68$ to $1\cdot75$ $\times 10^{11}$	25 to 30	640
Ferroxcube 7 A2	$-2\cdot3$ to $2\cdot8$ $\times 10^7$	$5\cdot5$ to $7\cdot5$ $\times 10^{-5}$		22 to 25	

N.B. The values of μ_i have been chosen for their optimum coupling efficiency. The above values are based on information given by Hueter and Bolt [5] and van der Burgt [29].

3.10. DYNAMIC CHARACTERISTICS OF MAGNETOSTRICTIVE OSCILLATORS

Dynamical relationships between electrical and mechanical quantities, similar to those for piezoelectric crystals, may be obtained for magnetostrictive transducers. The procedure is not straight-forward because difficulties arise when considering the exact nature of the magnetic flux linkage. Equation 3.51, however, shows that a mechanical force, F, acting on a rod of cross-sectional area, A, is related to the field, H, by the expression:

$$F = TA = \Lambda BA = \Lambda \mu_i A H \tag{3.53}$$

i.e., F is directly proportional to H. Furthermore, H is directly proportional to the exciting current, i, and the constant of proportionality depends only on the method of flux linkage, e.g. for a long solenoid having n turns per metre, $H = ni$, so that

$$F = D'i \tag{3.54}$$

where D' is a constant. Also, since the voltage, V, is equal to the rate of change of flux, we can assume that V is directly proportional to dB/dt and from equation 3.47 we have:

$$dB/dt = (1/\beta)\,(dS/dt) = u/\beta l \tag{3.55}$$

where l represents the original length of the rod. Thus V must be directly proportional to u. Since the coupling between F and i is identical with that between V and u, it is reasonable to assume that

$$V = D'u \tag{3.56}$$

The clamped electrical impedance, Z, of the transducer is given by

$$Z = \frac{V}{i} = \frac{uD'}{i} = \frac{VD'}{F} \tag{3.57}$$

i.e.:
$$F = a_T V \tag{3.58}$$

and
$$i = a_T u \tag{3.59}$$

Here, $a_T = D'/Z$ is the *transformation factor* similar to that used for piezoelectric transducers. One can now proceed with these electromechanical analogies in the same way as for piezoelectric oscillators. When considering equivalent circuits, losses due to hysteresis and the induction of eddy currents must be taken into account. Phase changes brought about by hysteresis must also be considered.

3.11. MAGNETOSTRICTIVE MATERIALS

Because magnetostrictive oscillators are used principally for high-power ultrasonic applications, an important consideration in the choice of a transducer is a high electromechanical coupling coefficient. However, much energy is dissipated in the form of heat, due to hysteresis and the induction of eddy currents; the transducer material should thus have a narrow hysteresis loop and a high electrical resistivity. The second requirement is not normally met by metals and some cooling device may be necessary to keep the temperature below the Curie point. Eddy current losses can be minimized by using laminated stacks which consist of alternate sheets of the metal and an insulating material, such as mica.

In recent years much work has been done in the development of ferrites as magnetostrictive elements. These are ceramic based oxides which have the chemical formula MFe_2O_4, where M represents a divalent metal ion such as nickel, zinc or lead having the cubic crystalline structure of the mineral spinel; these materials are often called *ferroxcubes*. Ferrites are non-metallic and eddy current losses are thus negligible. Their magnetostrictive coefficients are comparable with those of conventional ferromagnetic transducer materials but their mechanical properties are inferior.

3.12. THE DESIGN OF MAGNETOSTRICTIVE GENERATORS

High power magnetostrictive generators are designed for maximum transfer efficiency and suitability for the application required.

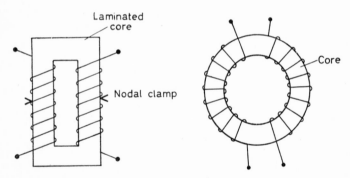

Figure 3.9. Window type transducer   *Figure 3.10.* Ring type transducer

The disadvantage of the rod-shaped oscillator is that there is a considerable leakage of magnetic flux. *Figures 3.9* and *3.10* illustrate two kinds of transducers arranged as closed magnetic circuits from which flux leakage is a minimum. *Figure 3.10* shows a ring type transducer which is commonly used for the cleaning of small parts and for the emulsification of liquids; the ring is wound with a toroidally-shaped coil so that the resultant oscillations are radial. The sound waves are thus brought to a focus at the centre of the coil where there is a maximum concentration of energy.

The practical upper limit for rod-shaped transducers vibrating at their fundamental frequencies is about 120 kc/s for low power outputs. For nickel, equation 3.45 shows that the corresponding length of the rod is about 2 cm. For high power outputs the effective upper frequency limit is about 40 kc/s. Theoretically, it is possible to generate high frequency radiation by exciting the transducer at an upper harmonic of its natural frequency, but this results in very much reduced outputs. Pierce overcame this difficulty by using a steel rod 9 cm long and 1·26 cm in diameter in which he had cut equidistant grooves, each 1 cm long (see *Figure 3.11*). Oscillations at a frequency of 300 kc/s were obtained, corresponding to those for a rod 0·9 cm long vibrating at its fundamental frequency. Another way of increasing the frequency is to use a hollow transducer and to fill it with some non-ferromagnetic material, such as lead, in which the velocity of sound is low. Because the velocity in lead is about

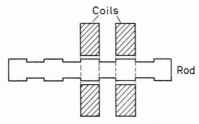

Figure 3.11. Magnetostrictive rod designed
by Pierce to operate at 300 kc/s

half that in nickel, a lead-filled nickel rod will oscillate at double the frequency of that for a solid nickel rod of similar length.

Where it is not possible to place the transducer in immediate contact with the work, as for the ultrasonic drill, some intermediate material is necessary and this must give a satisfactory matching of impedance. For the ultrasonic drill (see *Figure 3.12*) it is desirable for the tool to vibrate with maximum velocity amplitude. This is achieved by using a tapered rod which acts as an acoustic trans-former in the same manner as a loudspeaker horn (see, for example, Kinsler and Frey[14], p. 298). The rod is made of some material having a characteristic impedance matching that of the transducer to which it is rigidly fixed. For maximum transfer efficiency it is exactly one wavelength long and is clamped at the velocity node at a distance of a quarter-wavelength from the transducer. Similar types of coupling have been used for ceramic transducers.

Various kinds of tapered rod are illustrated in *Figure 3.12* and the simplest is a straightforward stepping, as shown in *Figure 3.12b*, but greater efficiency is achieved by using a conical, or better still, an exponential rod. Where a very large increase in velocity amplitude is desired, several cones may be arranged in series, as shown in *Figure 3.12d,* although the use of this device entails high energy losses.

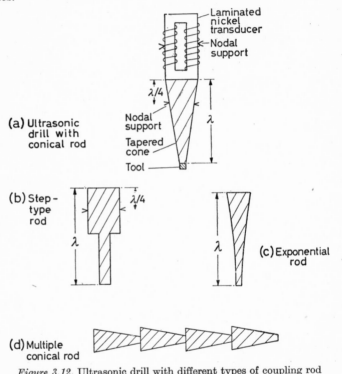

Figure 3.12. Ultrasonic drill with different types of coupling rod

3.13. MAGNETOSTRICTIVE RECEIVERS

Rods of ferromagnetic material may be used directly as probe receivers described under category (*b*) in Section 3.1, when they are immersed in sound fields in such a way that their end faces are normal to the direction of the waves. A rod of 0·5 mm diameter can be used in water without upsetting the wave configuration at frequencies up to about 300 kc/s, and reasonable results are possible at up to double this frequency.

For one design (see *Figure 3.13*) a nickel rod is held vertically in a fluid in which plane waves are propagated in an upward direction. The rod is covered with a plastic tube so that only the free end is exposed to the sound waves. These travel along the rod and cause a current to be induced in a winding at its upper end by the converse magnetostrictive effect. The rod is suitably polarized by a coil carrying a direct current. Standing waves in the rod may be eliminated, if this is considered desirable, by means of some absorbent material placed at the upper end.

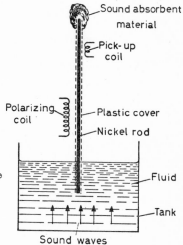

Figure 3.13. Magnetostrictive probe microphone for liquids

3.14. MECHANICAL GENERATORS

3.14.1. *General Considerations*

Mechanical generators are used primarily for the propagation of high energy ultrasonics in fluids. They can be classified under four headings, viz. cavity resonators, wedge resonators, vortex generators, and sirens. The first three types are commonly called ultrasonic whistles.

3.14.2. *Cavity Resonators*

When a fluid jet flows in the vicinity of a cavity the latter may be caused to vibrate at its natural frequencies. A well-known example of this is the production of a note from an empty bottle by blowing across its mouth. For a cylindrical cavity of length, l, the frequency, f, of the vibrations is given by the expression:

$$f = (2n-1)c/4(l+\delta) \qquad (3.60)$$

where c represents the velocity of sound in the fluid within the cavity, n an integer, and δ a quantity which depends only upon the diameter of the cylinder and the pressure exerted by the jet.

Galton, in 1883, was the first to use such a generator at ultrasonic frequencies and an improvement of his design was made by Edelmann in 1900. *Figure 3.14* illustrates a typical form of cavity resonator, known as the Galton whistle. The nozzle is terminated in an annular slit through which a current of air flows; this strikes a circular knife edge at one end of the cavity, causing the air within it to vibrate. The length of the cavity can be varied by moving a piston, the position of which is controlled by a micrometer screw. Another micrometer device controls the distance of separation of the annular slit and the circular knife edge.

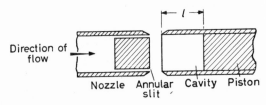

Figure 3.14. Diagram of Galton whistle

Now, the frequency of propagation is a function of the quantity, δ, which, in turn, depends upon the pressure of the jet. Because of the difficulty in maintaining a steady jet pressure it is not easy to obtain a constant frequency. The practical upper frequency limit is about 25 kc/s because, if one attempts to obtain higher frequencies, multiple edge tones having intensities of the same order as that of the fundamental note are produced. For hydrogen gas, in which the velocity of sound is about four times greater than in air, the upper frequency limit is about 100 kc/s. At the upper frequency limits power outputs are very small.

3.14.3. *The Hartmann Generator*

In 1927 Hartmann and Trolle designed a whistle which was capable of high outputs at ultrasonic frequencies. The nozzle, see *Figure 3.15a*, is conical in shape. This causes an increase in the pressure exerted by the fluid at the orifice by such an amount that the emergent jet travels at a supersonic speed. For air, an excess pressure of 0·9 atmosphere is sufficient for a speed of Mach 1. Shock waves are propagated at an angle to the forward direction and, consequently, are reflected from side to side of the jet (see *Figure 3.15b*).

Measurements of static pressure in the jet with a Pitot tube have shown periodic variations in the forward direction with maxima at points A, C, E, etc., and minima at B, D, etc. The regions in which the static pressure is rising, i.e. BC, DE, etc., are zones of instability, and, if one places the mouth of a cavity in such a region, resonance occurs. The corresponding frequency, f, depends on the respective

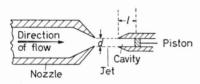

(a) Diagram of generator

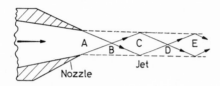

(b) Propagation of shock waves
in the jet

Figure 3.15. Hartmann generator

diameters of the jet and cavity, the length, l, of the cavity and the velocity, c, of sound in the fluid. In the special case where the diameter, d, of the jet is equal to that of the cavity, Hartmann showed that:

$$f = c/4(l + 0 \cdot 3d)$$

For example, for an air cavity of diameter 2·5 mm and length 2 mm, waves of a frequency of about 30 kc/s are generated. The power output depends upon the magnitude of the excess pressure and the diameter of the jet.

This device can produce cavitation at frequencies of up to more than 60 kc/s. As much as 50 watts acoustic power can be produced in air at a frequency of 20 kc/s. The efficiency is a maximum (around 5 per cent) when the mouth of the cavity lies just inside the first region of pressure instability and when the diameters of the cavity and jet are both equal to the length of the cavity.

73

3.14.4. Wedge Resonators

One form of wedge resonator is a solid plate with wedge-shaped edges, such as a razor blade (see *Figure 3.16*) placed in front of a nozzle. The emergent jet, similar to that used with the Hartmann generator, sets the wedge into flexural vibrations. The wedge which is clamped at one or more nodal points, will resonate when one

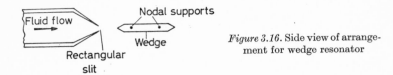

Figure 3.16. Side view of arrangement for wedge resonator

edge is in a region of instability. The resonant frequency, f, for a wedge mounted in the manner shown in *Figure 3.16* is given by the formula:

$$f = \frac{Cd}{l^2}\sqrt{\frac{Y}{\rho}}$$

where l represents the length of the wedge, d its thickness, Y and ρ the Young's modulus and density, respectively, for the material of the plate, and C is a numerical constant. Wedge resonators are used extensively for emulsification processes, especially in the food and cosmetic industries; the frequencies used are of the order of 30 kc/s.

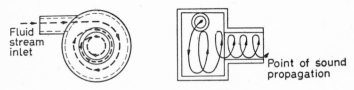

Figure 3.17. Vortex whistle (after Vonnegut[15])

3.14.5. Vortex Whistles

Figure 3.17 illustrates two sections of a vortex generator designed by Vonnegut[15]; this was intended for propagation into air but it can be adapted for liquids. Air is introduced tangentially into a 1-inch diameter cylinder and follows a helical path through an adjoining tube of about 0·3 inch diameter. In order to conserve angular momentum there is an increase in rotational speed and,

74

hence, frequency as the air stream passes into the smaller cylinder. Sound waves are propagated from the open end of the latter. The frequency of propagation, which depends on the rate of fluid flow, can be adjusted simply by varying the air pressure. At present, the upper frequency limit is about 15 kc/s.

3.14.6. Sirens

Sirens have proved very effective in producing high energy ultrasonic waves in fluids at frequencies of up to 30 kc/s and they have been shown to be especially useful for such applications as the coagulation of aerosols. The siren, in its simplest form, consists of a disc (the rotor) in which are drilled a number of similar holes

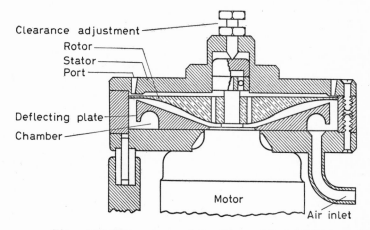

Figure 3.18. Ultrasonic siren (after Allen and Rudnick[16])

spaced equally around the circumference of a circle concentric with it. This disc is rotated in front of a similar disc (the stator) which is at rest, while jets of fluid are directed through the holes. These jets are interrupted by the rotation of the holes in the rotor, with the result that intermittent puffs of fluid are released and sound waves are thus propagated. The frequency of these waves is given by the product of the number of holes in the disc and the number of revolutions in unit time of the rotor.

Figure 3.18 illustrates a design by Allen and Rudnick[16] for propagating high energy ultrasonic waves. Both rotor and stator contained 100 perforations and the siren was driven by means of a 2/3 h.p. motor having a variable speed up to 340 revolutions per second (i.e. corresponding to a frequency of 34 kc/s). The adjacent surfaces of the stator and rotor were lapped to within 0·001 inch in order to reduce leakage of air. The apparatus was $11\frac{1}{2}$ inches high and $7\frac{1}{2}$ inches in diameter, weighed 55 lb. and was placed on rubber mountings to eliminate vibration.

3.15. MECHANICAL RECEIVERS

3.15.1. General Considerations

Mechanical receivers as used in ultrasonics have been, as far as the author is aware, applied only to fluid media. Two types of receivers are used, namely, those which determine the amplitude of one of the wave vectors and those which measure pressure of radiation (see Section 2.9). The latter type of instrument is commonly called a *Radiometer*.

3.15.2. Observations of Suspended Particles

The most direct method of obtaining acoustic intensities at points in a sound field is by observing suspended disperse particles such as cigarette smoke. These particles should, if they are not too heavy, be disturbed by the sound waves in the same way as the particles forming the medium, and their displacement amplitude should be related directly to the displacement amplitude for the medium. Smoke particle displacements in acoustic fields at audio-frequencies have been measured by Andrade and Parker[17] with a microscope. The method can be extended to lower ultrasonic frequencies, the upper frequency limit being determined by the response of the disperse particles to the sound vibrations. Care must be taken that the particles are sufficiently dispersed in order that coagulation does not occur (see Section 8.4). Because of the inertia of the particles, a correction factor which depends on frequency and the particle mass must be made to the observed value of the displacement amplitude.

3.15.3. The Rayleigh Disc

The Rayleigh disc is used for measuring particle velocity amplitude. It consists of a thin circular disc which is suspended vertically in the sound field by means of a torsion fibre. Initially the plane of the disc lies in the direction of propagation. The sound waves cause the disc to rotate to a position at right-angles to this direction. This motion is counteracted by the torque of the suspension and the disc comes to rest after rotating through an angle, θ. When the disc lies in a state of equilibrium, the angle is measured with an optical lever arrangement in which the mirror is either attached to the suspension

76

or forms the polished surface of the disc. Koenig showed (see, for example, Stephens and Bate[18], p. 247) that the torque, C, to a first approximation is given by the expression:

$$C = (4/3)\rho a^3 \xi^2_{RMS} \sin 2\theta$$

where a represents the radius of the disc and ξ^2_{RMS} the root mean square particle velocity. a should be small compared with wavelength.

3.15.4. Radiometers

The simplest form of radiometer is a tiny solid sphere suspended in a horizontal sound field. In the absence of radiation the sphere hangs vertically, and when the sound waves are propagated, the

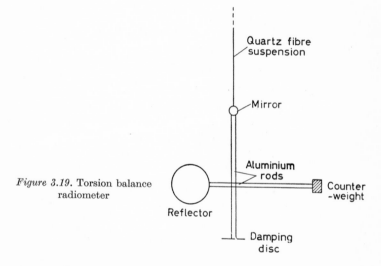

Figure 3.19. Torsion balance radiometer

pressure of radiation causes it to be displaced in a horizontal direction. The angle of displacement of the suspension depends on the pressure exerted, which (see Section 2.9) is related directly to the acoustic intensity at the position of the sphere. This device can be calibrated by subjecting the sphere to known fluid pressures.

Other radiometers are of the balance type (see *Figures 3.19* and *3.20*). They may be used as probes or placed at the end of the acoustic line. The essential part of the radiation balance is the reflector, and for use with progressive waves its dimensions must be small compared with wavelength. Highest sensitivity occurs when the characteristic impedance of the reflector has a value which gives a maximum mismatch of impedance for the reflector and the fluid. In this way maximum reflection occurs and the reaction of the reflector to the radiation pressure is greatest. With a gaseous medium a solid plate should be used but, where the medium is a

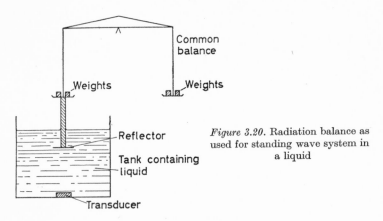

Figure 3.20. Radiation balance as used for standing wave system in a liquid

liquid, the most effective type of reflector consists of two thin sheets of solid material, such as mica, with an air space in between.

Figure 3.20 illustrates a common balance type of radiometer. Here the detector terminates the acoustic line and has dimensions which are of a higher order than the wavelength. This results in the formation of a stationary wave system. Maximum readings of

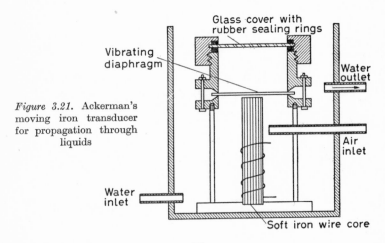

Figure 3.21. Ackerman's moving iron transducer for propagation through liquids

pressure occur when the position of the reflector is that for resonance and minimum readings when its position is that for anti-resonance.

3.16. ELECTROMAGNETIC TRANSDUCERS

Electromagnetic generators of both moving coil and moving iron types, which operate in a fashion similar to the loudspeaker, are commonly used for high-power applications at audio-frequencies; they can also be used at lower ultrasonic frequencies. These generators are described in some detail by Crawford[19] and by Hueter and Bolt[5].

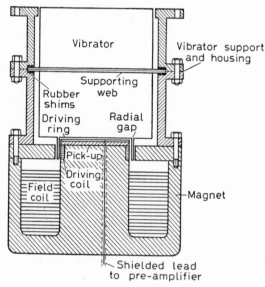

Figure 3.22. Diagrammatic representation of a moving coil electromagnetic transducer designed by St Clair for high frequency vibrations in gases

Because of their low fundamental resonant frequencies, the responses of these oscillators decrease rapidly above 10 kc/s and their outputs are comparatively low at 20 kc/s. Diagrams of moving coil and moving iron transducers are given in *Figures 3.21* and *3.22*, respectively.

For internal friction measurements at low amplitudes in solid bars, Giacomini (see Mason[13], p. 95) used electromagnetic transducers at frequencies ranging from a few cycles per second to several hundred kilocycles. An arrangement for longitudinal vibrations of a poorly conducting bar is illustrated in *Figure 3.23*. The bar was coated with a continuous strip of conducting material over opposite halves of the upper and lower surfaces and the adjoining end face. It was supported nodally by means of electrically conducting devices and the coated end placed in a horizontal magnetic field at right-angles to the axis of the bar. When an alternating current passed through the conducting strip, the bar vibrated longitudinally in accordance with Fleming's left-hand rule.

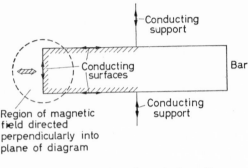

Figure 3.23. Giacomini's electromagnetic method for exciting a poorly conducting bar into ultrasonic vibrations

3.17. ELECTROSTATIC TRANSDUCERS

Electrostatic methods of generating both longitudinal and torsional vibrations of low amplitude have been used at frequencies of up to 300 kc/s and over wide ranges of temperature. When a steady potential difference is applied across two parallel metal plates, a force of attraction is experienced between them. On superimposing an alternating voltage of lower amplitude than this steady potential difference, the force of attraction varies sinusoidally at the same frequency as that of the applied voltage. If one of the plates is freely supported, the other vibrates at that frequency.

An electrostatic transducer is reversible and may thus be used as a microphone. The plate in contact with the sound field vibrates, when excited, thus giving rise to a periodic change in capacitance. When the microphone is connected in series with a high resistance and given a polarizing voltage, these periodic changes in capacitance appear as periodic changes in voltage across the resistance.

Bordoni (see Section 6.12) has used the electrostatic method for generating ultrasonic vibrations in solids for internal friction measurements. Schodder and others [20, 21] have developed electrostatic transducers with solid dielectrics for use in air and water.

3.18. THERMAL TRANSDUCERS

3.18.1. Thermal Generators

Thermal generators are not commonly used as ultrasonic sources. However, two kinds of thermal ultrasonic generators are worth mentioning. The first is the *spark-gap generator*. When an alternating potential difference of a given frequency, f, is applied across a spark gap, periodic temperature changes of frequency, $2f$, occur. The wave-form is that of an unsmoothed rectified sine curve but if a sufficiently high polarizing voltage is applied, the frequency of the resultant sound waves is f, and the wave-form is approximately sinusoidal. The spark-gap generator has been used as a 'white noise' source for investigating the acoustic properties of scaled-down models of auditoria, using the reverberation technique; a pulse of 'white noise' is emitted by connecting a damped oscillating circuit across the gap. The spark-gap generator has been used to radiate frequencies of up to 2 Mc/s (see Bergmann[2], p. 4).

The other type of thermal generator is the *thermophone* (see Beranek[22]). This has been used at audio frequencies as a standard source and has been applied to propagating ultrasonic waves through liquid helium (see Section 5.6). It consists of a strip of metal, such as platinum, through which an alternating current is passed. Periodic variations of temperature occur twice per current cycle for an unpolarized strip and once per cycle where the strip is polarized by the application of a direct current.

3.18.2. Thermal Receivers

Thermal receivers, on the other hand, have important applications to ultrasonics. One type, the hot-wire microphone, measures particle velocity amplitude, and others, described here as 'acoustic calorimeters', measure the heating effect of the sound energy.

3.18.3. The Hot-wire Microphone

The hot-wire microphone was originally developed by Tucker during the 1914–18 war for the location of guns. Its subsequent use as an ultrasonic receiver was largely due to Richardson.[23] When a wire heated to just below redness is placed in a fluid stream, the resultant cooling causes a drop in its electrical resistance. Where the fluid flow is alternating there are two components of the change in resistance.

One of these is periodic having the same frequency as the waves, and the other is a steady decrease. At ultrasonic frequencies only the steady fall in resistance can be observed, because the time period is too short to allow for any response to the alternating changes.

The particle velocity amplitude in a sound field can be determined by measuring this fall in resistance, to which it is directly proportional. Richardson, using this method, investigated the intensity distribution in stationary waves in gases at frequencies up to 600 kc/s. He used a nickel or platinum wire, 0·001 inch diameter and 0·5 inch long, which was held between the metal prongs of a fork. This method has not met with much success for liquids because of the low sensitivity due to convection losses.

3.18.4. Acoustic Calorimeters

Heat energy is liberated when ultrasonic waves pass through a material which is absorbent. The quantity of heat dissipated at any point in a sound field is proportional to the intensity.

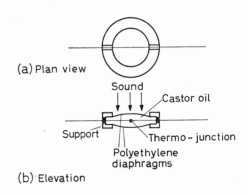

Figure 3.24. Thermocouple probe (after Dunn and Fry[24])

Calorimetric methods of measuring intensities in liquids have been reported by Dunn and Fry.[24] A thermocouple was embedded in a liquid cell (see *Figure 3.24*) arranged with its faces normal to the sound waves. The material of the cell and the liquid inside it were chosen for their characteristic impedances to match, as closely as possible, that of the liquid under test. In this way reflection at the interfaces was reduced to a minimum. The liquid in the cell had a high absorption coefficient so that as much heat energy as possible was liberated.

The thermocouple wire had a diameter of 0·0005 inch, which at a frequency of 1 Mc/s is equal to about one-hundredth part of a wavelength and its output terminals were connected, via an amplifier, to a cathode ray oscilloscope fitted with a camera. The source was excited by means of a simple square-wave pulse for a period of one second and the resultant temperature increase, which is proportional to the intensity, was recorded by the thermocouple. The instrument was calibrated with a suspended sphere radiometer.

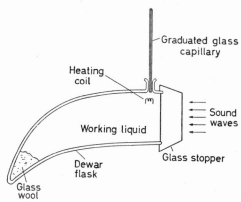

Figure 3.25. Meter for measuring ultrasonic energy (after Mikhailov and Shutilov[25])

A method suitable for measuring the overall sound energy in a finite medium which was devised by Mikhailov and Shutilov[25] is depicted in *Figure 3.25*. The heat liberated by the sound is absorbed by the liquid in the flask. This causes expansion and the liquid rises up the glass capillary tube. The shape of the flask is arranged in such a way that there is no reflection back into the acoustic field. Sound waves which are transmitted through the liquid are finally absorbed by the glass wool at the end of the vessel. The instrument may be calibrated by means of a heating coil. Measurements of intensity ranging from 0·05 to 30 W/cm² were obtained with errors not greater than 10 per cent.

3.19. CHEMICAL DETECTORS

Ultrasonic radiation of sufficiently high intensity may be detected by means of the chemical effects produced, some of which are described in Section 8.8. Most of these, however, do not provide a reliable quantitative measurement of intensity or wave-vector amplitudes. One important exception is the *electrokinetic effect* which has been used for the operation of ultrasonic microphones in dilute electrolytic solutions.

The electrokinetic effect has been described by Dietrick, Yaeger, Bugosh and Hovorka.[26] If a wire covered with a porous or fibrous material is immersed in a dilute electrolytic solution through which ultrasonic waves are propagated, an alternating potential difference having the same frequency as that of the waves is developed between

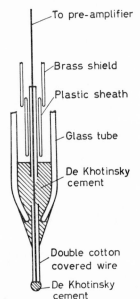

To pre-amplifier

Brass shield

Plastic sheath

Glass tube

De Khotinsky cement

Double cotton covered wire

De Khotinsky cement

Figure 3.26. Electrokinetic microphone (after Dietrick *et al.*[26])

the wire and the solution. They found that the effect was displayed most effectively with double cotton-covered wire. An electrokinetic microphone of their design is illustrated in *Figure 3.26*. Because of the small dimensions of the receiving element, measurements could be made without difficulty at frequencies of some hundreds of kilocycles. For pulsed waves of frequency 200 kc/s in 0·001 molar sodium chloride solution, the open-circuit E.M.F. developed in a double cotton-covered copper wire was of the order of 10^{-7} volt per dyne cm^{-2} of acoustic pressure.

3.20. OPTICAL DETECTORS

In Section 5.11.3 it is shown that a parallel beam of ultrasonic waves acts as a diffraction grating for light and that the decrease in intensity of the zeroth order spectrum varies directly with the acoustic intensity. The spectral intensity as measured by a photo-electric cell thus determines the acoustic intensity in the beam.

3.21. DEPLETION LAYER TRANSDUCERS

White[30] has described a method of propagating ultrasonic waves in a piezoelectric semiconductor, such as gallium arsenide or cadmium sulphide, where a thin depletion layer is introduced into the material. By this method it has been found possible to generate and detect waves having frequencies ranging from about 300 Mc/s to tens of thousands of megacycles per second.

A depletion layer in an extrinsic semiconductor is a region having a very low resultant carrier concentration and thus a high resistance. It may be produced in one of two ways. One can introduce into the material a p-n junction which is reverse-biased with a direct voltage. Alternatively, for an n-type semiconductor, the end surface of the specimen can be plated with an electrode of metal or p-type semiconductor and a reverse bias applied as before. The piezoelectric properties of such a depletion layer are similar to those possessed by crystal transducers; its thickness and, hence, resonant frequency are dependent upon the value of the applied direct voltage. The transducer formed in this way can be excited either at resonance or off-resonance by the application of an alternating voltage. Typical values of thickness range from 10^{-3} to 10^{-5} cm, which correspond to a fundamental frequency range of approximately 300 Mc/s to 30,000 Mc/s.

REFERENCES

1. VIGOUREUX, P. and BOOTH, C. F. *Quartz Vibrators and their Applications*, H.M.S.O., London, 1950
2. BERGMANN, L. *Ultrasonics* (trans. H. S. Hatfield), Wiley, New York/ Bell, London, 1938
3. BÖMMEL, H. E. and DRANSFELD, K. *Phys. Rev. (letters)*, 1958, **2**, 298
4. CADY, W. G. *Piezoelectricity*, McGraw-Hill, New York, 1946
5. HUETER, T. F. and BOLT, R. H. *Sonics*, Wiley, New York/Chapman and Hall, London, 1955
6. MASON, W. P. *Piezoelectric Crystals and their Application to Ultrasonics*, van Nostrand, New York, 1950
7. CRAWFORD, A. E. *Brit. J. Appl. Phys.*, 1961, **12**, 529
8. BECHMANN, R. *J. Sci. Instrum.*, 1952, **29**, 73
9. JAFFE, B., ROTH, R. S., and MARZULLO, S. *J. Appl. Phys.*, 1954, **25**, 809

10. ANAN'EVA, A. A. *Zh. Akust.* (*U.S.S.R.*), 1959, **5**, 14 (Eng. transl. *Sov. Phys. J. Acoustics*, 1959, **5**, 13)
11. HATFIELD, P. *Acustica*, 1954, **4**, 193
12. ANAN'EVA, A. A. *Zh. Akust.* (*U.S.S.R.*), 1956, **2**, 10 (Eng. transl. *Sov. Phys., J. Acoustics*, 1956, **2**, 8)
13. MASON, W. P. *Physical Acoustics and the Properties of Solids*, van Nostrand, New York, 1958
14. KINSLER, L. E. and FREY, P. *Fundamentals of Acoustics*, Wiley, New York/Chapman and Hall, London, 1950
15. VONNEGUT, B. *J. acoust. Soc. Amer.*, 1954, **26**, 18
16. ALLEN, C. H. and RUDNICK, I. *J. acoust. Soc. Amer.*, 1947, **19**, 857
17. ANDRADE, E. N. da C. and PARKER, R. C. *Proc. Roy. Soc.*, 1937, **159**, 507
18. STEPHENS, R. W. B. and BATE, A. E. *Wave Motion and Sound*, Arnold, London, 1950
19. CRAWFORD, A. E. *Ultrasonic Engineering*, Butterworths, London, 1955
20. KUHL, W., SCHODDER, G. R., and SCHRÖDER, F-K. *Acustica*, 1954, **4**, 519
21. SCHODDER, G. R. and WIEKHORST, F. *Acustica*, 1957, **7**, 38
22. BERANEK, L. L. *Acoustic Measurements*, Wiley, New York, 1949
23. RICHARDSON, E. G. *Ultrasonic Physics*, 2nd Edn., Elsevier, Amsterdam, 1962
24. DUNN, F. and FRY, W. J. *Trans. I.R.E.*, 1957, PGUE **5**, 59
25. MIKHAILOV, I. G. and SHUTILOV, V. A. *Zh. Akhust* (*U.S.S.R.*), 1957, **3**, 370 (Eng. transl. *Sov. Phys. J. Acoustics*, 1957, **3**, 410)
26. DIETRICK, H. *et al. J. Acoust. Soc. Amer.*, 1953, **25**, 461
27. CARLIN, B. *Ultrasonics*, 2nd Edn., McGraw-Hill, New York, 1960
28. VAN DER BURGT, C. M. *Electronic Technology*, 1960, **37**, 330
29. VAN DER BURGT, C. M. *Philips Tech. Rev.*, 1956/7, **18**, 285 and *Matronics*, Sept., 1958, No. 15, p. 273
30. WHITE, D. L. I.R.E. *International Convention Board*, 1961, Part 6, p. 304

LOW AMPLITUDE PROPAGATION IN GASES

4.1. VELOCITIES IN GASES

GASES cannot resist shear stresses and, for that reason, only longitudinal waves can be propagated through them. Now, reversible adiabatic changes for ideal gases are expressed by the equation:

$$PV^\gamma = P/\rho^\gamma = \text{constant}$$

where P represents the pressure, V the volume, ρ the density and γ the ratio of the principal specific heats.

Differentiating this equation gives:

$$\left(\frac{\partial P}{\partial \rho}\right)_S = \frac{\gamma P}{\rho}$$

and this combined with equation 2.28 yields the expression for the speed of sound through an ideal gas, viz.:

$$c = \left(\frac{\gamma P}{\rho}\right)^{\frac{1}{2}} \tag{4.1}$$

The equation of state for one mole of an ideal gas is commonly expressed in the form:

$$PV = RT \tag{4.2}$$

where T represents the absolute temperature and R the universal gas constant. Equation 4.1 may then be rewritten as:

$$c = (\gamma RT/M)^{\frac{1}{2}} \tag{4.3}$$

where M represents the molecular weight. Equation 4.3 shows that, provided γ remains constant, the speed of sound in an ideal gas is a function of temperature only and should stay constant for changes in pressure. Measurements for 'permanent' gases, such as oxygen and nitrogen, at normal pressures and low frequencies have confirmed this relationship to a high degree of approximation.

Equation 4.3 holds only approximately for non-ideal gases and a discrepancy is noticeable for organic vapours. For a non-ideal gas one can conveniently express the equation of state as:

$$PV = RT + BP \tag{4.4}$$

where B represents the second virial coefficient (see for example, Roberts and Miller[1], p. 114). From equation 2.29 the velocity of sound is then expressed approximately as:

$$c = \{\gamma(RT + 2BP)/M\}^{\frac{1}{2}} \qquad (4.5)$$

Values of acoustic velocities and a number of gases at $0°$ C are given in *Table 4.1*.

4.2. ABSORPTION AND VELOCITY DISPERSION IN GASES

Classical theory predicts that sound waves are absorbed in gases as a result of *viscosity*, as shown by Stokes (1841) and *thermal conduction*, as predicted by Kirchhoff (1868). Measurements of absorption coefficients at ultrasonic frequencies have indicated that attenuation in monatomic gases, such as argon and xenon, is due only to these phenomena. For polyatomic gases, however, values greater than those predicted by classical theory have been obtained. In 1928, Herzfeld and Rice showed that an additional factor, *thermal relaxation*, must be taken into account. Each of these three causes of absorption have proved to be relaxational in origin.

Table 4.1. Calculated Values of Acoustic Velocities, Classical Relaxation Times, and Classical Absorption Coefficients ($\omega\tau \ll 1$) for Gases at S.T.P.

Gas	Velocity m sec^{-1}	Relaxation time $\times 10^{-10}$ sec		Absorption Coefficient $\times 10^{-13}$ neper cm^{-1}/sec^2		
		Viscosity	Thermal conduction	Viscosity	Thermal conduction	Total
	c	τ_{vis}	τ_{th}	a_{vis}/f^2	a_{th}/f^2	a_{class}/f^2
Air	330	1·6	0·70	0·96	0·42	1·4
Argon	320	1·5	1·1	0·96	0·68	1·6
Carbon Dioxide	260	1·4	0·49	1·0	0·30	1·3
Helium	970	1·5	1·1	0·30	0·22	0·52
Hydrogen	1,300	0·74	0·31	0·11	0·047	0·16
Neon	430	2·4	1·7	1·1	0·82	1·9
Nitrogen	330	2·9	1·1	1·7	0·68	2·4
Oxygen	310	1·9	0·78	1·2	0·49	1·7

The values of τ and a/f^2 have been calculated from data given by Kaye and Laby[14] using equations 4.11, 4.25, 4.12, and 4.26.

4.3. CLASSICAL THEORY OF ABSORPTION IN GASES

4.3.1. Viscosity

Viscosity is a property of a fluid which corresponds to shear elasticity in solids. The relationship between the applied shear stress and the resultant deformation for a solid, assuming Hooke's law to be obeyed, is given by the equation:

$$F_T/A = G_S S_T \tag{4.6}$$

where F_T is a force applied tangentially to the solid surface over an area A, S_T is the resultant shear strain and G_s is the corresponding adiabatic modulus of irigidity.

Where a shear stress is applied to a fluid, the latter collapses because of its inability to support such a stress. This collapse takes a finite time, which depends on the coefficient of viscosity, η. Newton showed for non-turbulent conditions, that:

$$F_T/A = \eta \dot{S}_T \tag{4.7}$$

where $\dot{S}_T$ is the velocity gradient caused by the shear stress.

In Section 6.1 it is shown that when longitudinal waves pass through an 'infinite' solid the compression stresses are accompanied by related shear stresses and the velocity of such waves is given by the relationship:

$$c^2 = (K_S = \tfrac{4}{3} G_S)/\rho$$

where K_S represents the adiabatic bulk modulus.

The wave equation 2.19 may then be rewritten as:

$$\frac{\partial^2 \xi}{\partial t^2} = \frac{K_S}{\rho}\frac{\partial^2 \xi}{\partial x^2} + \frac{4}{3}\frac{G_S}{\rho}\frac{\partial^2 \xi}{\partial x^2} \tag{4.8}$$

The corresponding equation for velocities in fluids is:

$$c^2 = K_S/\rho$$

in which there is no term involving shear elasticity. The related wave equation is:

$$\frac{\partial^2 \xi}{\partial t^2} = \frac{K_s}{\rho}\frac{\partial^2 \xi}{\partial x^2} \tag{4.9}$$

If, however, one considers viscosity, which occurs as a result of the action of the shear component of the longitudinal waves, equation 4.9 can be modified to give an expression similar in form to equation 4.8. Thus η is substituted for G_S and, since $\dot{S}_T$ corresponds to S_T, we may write $\dot{\xi}$ for ξ in the second term on the right-hand side.

Hence:
$$\frac{\partial^2 \xi}{\partial t^2} = \frac{K_S}{\rho}\frac{\partial^2 \xi}{\partial x^2} + \frac{4}{3}\frac{\eta}{\rho}\frac{\partial^2 \dot{\xi}}{\partial x^2} \tag{4.10}$$

or
$$\frac{\partial^2 \xi}{\partial t^2} = c^2 \frac{\partial^2 \xi}{\partial x^2} + \frac{4}{3}\frac{\eta}{\rho}\frac{\partial^2 \dot{\xi}}{\partial x^2} \tag{4.10a}$$

This is identical with equation 2.43 if one substitutes $r = \frac{4}{3}\eta$, i.e. viscosity may be regarded as a relaxational phenomenon. The corresponding relaxation time, τ, is given by the expression:

$$\tau = \frac{r}{\rho c^2} = \frac{4}{3}\frac{\eta}{\rho c^2} \tag{4.11}$$

Calculated values of τ for some of the more common gases at S.T.P. are given in *Table 4.1*. These are seen to be of the order of 10^{-10} sec, which corresponds to a frequency of about 1,000 Mc/s. Oscillations of this frequency are extremely difficult to generate in gases, for which an upper limit of only about 10 Mc/s is generally possible. Hence the condition, $\omega\tau \ll 1$, is usually satisfied and from equation 2.46b we have:

$$a_{\text{vis}} = \frac{\omega^2 \tau}{2c} = \frac{8\pi^2}{3}\left(\frac{\eta}{\rho c^3}\right)f^2 \tag{4.12}$$

Some calculated values of a_{vis}/f^2, which is constant for a given material in a given state, are given in *Table 4.1*.

4.3.2. Thermal Conduction

In Section 2.10.2 thermal conduction was discussed as a relaxational process. We shall now derive expressions for the corresponding relaxation time and absorption coefficient.

Consider a thin parallel layer of the medium (see *Figure 2.3*) having a thickness, δx, and situated at a distance, x, from some origin, and let plane longitudinal waves be propagated at right-angles to this layer. Let ξ, p, and T represent particle displacement, acoustic pressure, and temperature at the boundary, A, of the layer and $\xi + \frac{\partial \xi}{\partial x}\delta x$, $p + \frac{\partial p}{\partial x}\delta x$, and $T + \frac{\partial T}{\partial x}\delta T$ be the respective values at the boundary, B. The rate of flow of heat per unit mass into the layer at A in a direction normal to the boundary is given by the expression:

$$\left(\frac{dQ}{dt}\right)_x = -\left(\frac{K}{\rho\delta x}\right)\frac{\partial T}{\partial x}$$

where K represents the coefficient of thermal conductivity. The rate of flow of heat per unit mass leaving the layer at B is then:

$$\left(\frac{dQ}{dt}\right)_{x+\delta x} = \left(\frac{dQ}{dt}\right)_x + \frac{\partial}{\partial x}\left(\frac{dQ}{dt}\right)_x \delta x$$

Hence the rate of absorption of heat per unit mass of the layer is expressed by:

$$\frac{dq}{dt} = \left(\frac{dQ}{dt}\right)_x - \left(\frac{dQ}{dt}\right)_{x+\delta x} = \frac{K}{\rho}\frac{\partial^2 T}{\partial x^2} \tag{4.13}$$

Let the temperature of an element of the layer be raised by an amount, dT, in two stages. The first stage brings the temperature up by a quantity, dT_1, at constant pressure, and is accompanied by a volume increase of dV. For the second stage there is a temperature increase, at constant volume, to the final value and an increase, dP, in pressure. The quantity, dq, of heat per unit mass which is absorbed during this operation is given by the expression:

$$dq = c_p dT_1 + c_v(dT - dT_1) \tag{4.14}$$

where c_p and c_v represent the specific heats of the gas at constant pressure and volume, respectively.

Because T is a single-valued function of P and ρ we have:

$$dT = \left(\frac{\partial T}{\partial \rho}\right)_P d\rho + \left(\frac{\partial T}{\partial P}\right)_\rho dP \tag{4.15}$$

and since dT_1 is the temperature change at constant volume, i.e. at constant ρ_o,

$$dT_1 = \left(\frac{\partial T}{\partial \rho}\right)_P d\rho$$

Thus from equation 4.14:

$$\frac{dq}{dt} = (c_p - c_v)\frac{\partial T_1}{\partial t} + c_v\frac{\partial T}{\partial t}$$

$$= c_v\left\{\frac{\partial T}{\partial t} + (\gamma - 1)\left(\frac{\partial T}{\partial \rho}\right)_P \frac{\partial \rho}{\partial t}\right\}$$

$$= \frac{K}{\rho}\frac{\partial^2 T}{\partial x^2} \tag{4.16}$$

from equation 4.13 (putting $\gamma = c_p/c_v$). Equation 4.15 gives:

$$\frac{\partial^2 T}{\partial x^2} = \left(\frac{\partial T}{\partial \rho}\right)_P \frac{\partial^2 \rho}{\partial x^2} + \left(\frac{\partial T}{\partial P}\right)_\rho \frac{\partial^2 P}{\partial x^2} \tag{4.17}$$

and:

$$\frac{\partial T}{\partial t} = \left(\frac{\partial T}{\partial \rho}\right)_P \frac{\partial \rho}{\partial t} + \left(\frac{\partial T}{\partial P}\right)_\rho \frac{\partial P}{\partial t} \tag{4.18}$$

Substituting these values into equation 4.16 we have:

$$\frac{K}{\rho}\left\{\left(\frac{\partial T}{\partial \rho}\right)_P \frac{\partial^2 \rho}{\partial x^2} + \left(\frac{\partial T}{\partial P}\right)_\rho \frac{\partial^2 P}{\partial x^2}\right\} =$$

$$c_v\left\{\left(\frac{\partial T}{\partial \rho}\right)_P \frac{\partial \rho}{\partial t} + \left(\frac{\partial T}{\partial P}\right)_\rho \frac{\partial P}{\partial t} + (\gamma - 1)\ \left(\frac{\partial T}{\partial \rho}\right)_P \frac{\partial \rho}{\partial t}\right\} \quad (4.19)$$

By considering the variation of P with ρ at constant temperature in equation 4.15 we see that:

$$\left(\frac{\partial T}{\partial \rho}\right)_P = -\left(\frac{\partial P}{\partial \rho}\right)_T \left(\frac{\partial T}{\partial P}\right)_\rho \quad (4.20)$$

Substituting this into equation 4.19 and rearranging, we obtain:

$$\frac{K}{\rho}\left\{\frac{\partial^2 P}{\partial x^2} - \left(\frac{\partial P}{\partial \rho}\right)_T \frac{\partial^2 \rho}{\partial x^2}\right\} = c_v\left\{\frac{\partial P}{\partial t} - \gamma\left(\frac{\partial P}{\partial \rho}\right)_T \frac{\partial \rho}{\partial t}\right\} \quad (4.21)$$

Now equation 2.29 states that:

$$\left(\frac{\partial P}{\partial \rho}\right)_T = c^2/\gamma$$

Substituting this into equation 4.21 we have:

$$\frac{\partial P}{\partial t} - c^2\frac{\partial \rho}{\partial t} = \frac{K}{\rho c_v}\left\{\frac{\partial^2 P}{\partial x^2} - \frac{c}{\gamma}\frac{\partial^2 \rho}{\partial x^2}\right\} \quad (4.22)$$

Since we are considering only changes of the various quantities we can write dp for dP and ρds for dρ, where these changes are due to the passage of sound waves through the gas. Hence:

$$\frac{\partial p}{\partial t} - c^2\rho\frac{\partial s}{\partial t} = \frac{K}{\rho c_v}\left\{\frac{\partial^2 p}{\partial x^2} - \frac{c^2\rho}{\gamma}\frac{\partial^2 s}{\partial x^2}\right\}$$

If we now make the substitutions $\dfrac{\partial p}{\partial x} = \rho\dfrac{\partial^2 \xi}{\partial t^2}$ and $s = -\dfrac{\partial \xi}{\partial x}$ (see Section 2.5) and then differentiate both sides with respect to x, we obtain:

$$\rho\frac{\partial^3 \xi}{\partial t^3} - c^2\rho\frac{\partial^3 \xi}{\partial x^2 \partial t} = \frac{K}{\rho c_v}\left\{\rho\frac{\partial^4 \xi}{\partial x^2 \partial t^2} - \frac{c^2\rho}{\gamma}\frac{\partial^4 \xi}{\partial x^4}\right\}$$

i.e.:

$$\frac{\partial}{\partial t}\left\{\frac{\partial^2 \xi}{\partial t^2} - c^2\frac{\partial^2 \xi}{\partial x^2}\right\} = \frac{K}{\rho c_v}\frac{\partial}{\partial x^2}\left\{\frac{\partial^2 \xi}{\partial t^2} - \frac{c^2}{\gamma}\frac{\partial^2 \xi}{\partial x^2}\right\} \quad (4.23)$$

Now one can substitute the wave equation: $\dfrac{\partial^2 \xi}{\partial t^2} = c^2 \dfrac{\partial^2 \xi}{\partial x^2}$ into the right-hand side of equation 4.23 without involving any first order errors. Hence:

$$\frac{\partial}{\partial t}\left\{ \frac{\partial^2 \xi}{\partial t^2} - c^2 \frac{\partial^2 \xi}{\partial x^2} \right\} = \frac{K}{\rho c_v} \frac{\partial}{\partial x^2}\left\{ \frac{\gamma - 1}{\gamma} \frac{\partial^2 \xi}{\partial t^2} \right\}$$

Integrating this with respect to t gives:

$$\frac{\partial^2 \xi}{\partial t^2} = c^2 \frac{\partial^2 \xi}{\partial x^2} + \frac{K}{\rho c_v} \frac{\gamma - 1}{\gamma} \frac{\partial^2 \xi}{\partial x^2} \qquad (4.24)$$

This equation is identical in form with equation 2.43, the solution being

$$\xi = \xi_0 \exp.(-ax)\exp. j\,(\omega t - kx)$$

Hence:

$$r = \frac{K}{\rho c_v} \frac{\gamma - 1}{\gamma}$$

giving the relaxation time:

$$\tau = \frac{r}{\rho c^2} = \frac{K}{\rho c^2 c_v} \frac{\gamma - 1}{\gamma} \qquad (4.25)$$

Calculated values of τ for a number of the more common gases are given in *Table 4.1*. As in the case of viscous relaxation, these are of the order of 10^{-10} sec. This corresponds again to a relaxation frequency of about 1,000 Mc/s which is outside the range of normal measurements for gases. Hence we can assume that $\omega\tau \ll 1$, so that:

$$a_{th} \simeq \frac{\omega^2 \tau}{2c} = \frac{2\pi^2 K}{\rho c^3 c_v} \frac{\gamma - 1}{\gamma} f^2 \qquad (4.26)$$

Comparing equations 4.12 and 4.26 we see that:

$$\frac{a_{th}}{a_{vis}} = \frac{3}{4} \frac{K}{\eta c_v} \frac{\gamma - 1}{\gamma} \qquad (4.27)$$

The absorption coefficient due to the combined effects of viscosity and thermal conduction is expressed as a_{class}, i.e.:

$$a_{class} = a_{vis} + a_{th}$$

and equations 4.12 and 4.26 show that the ratio a_{class}/f^2 is a constant for a given material in a given physical state. Values of a_{vis}/f^2, a_{th}/f^2, and a_{class}/f^2 for a number of gases are given in *Table 4.1*.

4.4. ABSORPTION AND VELOCITY DISPERSION DUE TO THERMAL RELAXATION

It is shown in textbooks on heat (see, for example, Roberts and Miller[1], p. 202) that the specific heat of a gas is determined by the number of degrees of freedom possessed by its molecules. These degrees of freedom are of two kinds, namely external and internal. External degrees of freedom, of which there are three per molecule, occur for translational motion and exist for all kinds of molecules. The energy of these degrees of freedom is exchanged between molecules by collision processes with negligible time delay. Internal degrees of freedom exist for rotational and vibrational motion of the molecules and may be excited by energy transfers from external modes for which finite time delays may occur; these occur only for polyatomic molecules. The rotations take place about defined axes and the vibrations are those of the atoms within the molecules.

The Principle of Equipartition of Energy shows that the molar heat, C_v, of an ideal gas at constant volume is equal to $nR/2$, where R is the universal gas constant and n represents the average number of degrees of freedom excited in each molecule. For a monatomic gas, such as argon, there are only the three external degrees of freedom per molecule. In this case C_v has a value, $3R/2$, and $\gamma = C_p/C_v = 5/3$, where C_p is the molar heat at constant pressure.

A diatomic gas can possess altogether seven degrees of freedom per molecule, three of which are translational, two rotational, and two vibrational, with the result that possible values of C_v and γ are $7R/2$ and $9/7$, respectively. For other polyatomic gases the number of possible degrees of freedom and, hence, their specific heats will depend upon the number of atoms in the molecules and the structure of the latter.

The measured value of the molar heat of a gas may not agree with the theoretical value as computed from the foregoing argument. This is because the internal degrees of freedom can be excited only by discrete changes of energy from one level to another, in accordance with quantum theory. Hence a particular internal degree of freedom of a molecule cannot be excited if insufficient energy is available for a transition from the ground state to the next energy level. This means that at temperatures below a characteristic value, Θ, which depends on the nature of the gas, there is very little chance that a given degree of freedom will be excited. For hydrogen, for example, the respective values of Θ for rotational and vibrational degrees of freedom are 60° K and 5,958° K. Hence, at temperatures below 60° K, hydrogen behaves as a monatomic gas, for which $C_v = 3R/2$. At temperatures between this value and 5,958° K, $C_v = 5R/2$. For statistical reasons the transitions at the temperatures, Θ, between the values of specific heat are gradual.

Energy exchanges between external and internal degrees of freedom require a finite time, characteristic of the nature of the process. Thus where acoustic energy is taken up by one of the internal modes, relaxation occurs. This is called *thermal relaxation* and a simplified theory of its effect on ultrasonic waves is discussed below.

4.5. SIMPLIFIED THEORY OF ABSORPTION IN GASES DUE TO THERMAL RELAXATION

Supposing that the molecules of an ideal gas contain two states of energy, i.e. (1) the ground state, being translational and (2) one of the excited internal states. Let their values be W and $W + \Delta W$, respectively. For equilibrium let there be n_1 molecules per mole in state 1 and n_2 molecules in state 2.

i.e.
$$n_1 + n_2 = N \tag{4.28}$$

where N, Avagadro's number, is constant. The effect of the sound wave is to alter the numbers n_1 to $n_1 + \Delta n_1$ and n_2 to $n_2 + \Delta n_2$, respectively, in a time Δt.

i.e.
$$n_1 + \Delta n_1 + n_2 + \Delta n_2 = N \tag{4.29}$$

Under conditions of equilibrium, let the average number of transitions per second from state 1 to state 2 be k_{12} and that from state 2 to state 1 be k_{21}. Hence the average rate of change, $\dot{n}_2$, of the molecules in the excited state is given by:

$$\dot{n}_2 = n_1 k_{12} + n_2 k_{21} \tag{4.30}$$

Now, because of excitation by the sound wave, n_2 changes to $n_2 + \Delta n_2$ in the time Δt.

i.e.:
$$\dot{n}_2 + \Delta \dot{n}_2 = (n_1 + \Delta n_1)\ (k_{12} + \Delta k_{12}) - (n_2 + \Delta n_2)\ (k_{21} + \Delta k_{21})$$

or:
$$\Delta \dot{n}_2 = n_1 \Delta k_{12} + k_{12} \Delta n_1 - n_2 \Delta k_{21} - k_{21} \Delta n_2 \tag{4.31}$$

But subtracting 4.28 from 4.29 gives $\Delta n_1 = -\Delta n_2$, and since $n_2 = 0$ for conditions of equilibrium we have:

$$\frac{n_2}{n_1} = \frac{k_{12}}{k_{21}} = \exp.(-\Delta W / \kappa T) \tag{4.32}$$

assuming that the distribution of molecules is described by classical statistics. Here κ represents Boltzmann's constant and T the absolute temperature.

Differentiation of equation 4.32 gives:

$$\Delta k_{12} = \exp.(-\Delta W / \kappa T)(\Delta k_{21} + k_{21} \Delta W_1 \Delta T / \kappa T^2)$$

and substituting these conditions into equation 4.31 yields:

$$\Delta \dot{n}_2 = n_2 k_{21} \Delta W . \Delta T / \kappa T^2 - \Delta n_2 (k_{12} + k_{21}) \tag{4.33}$$

If one writes $\mathrm{d}(\Delta n_2)/\mathrm{d}t$ for $\Delta \dot{n}_2$, this is seen to be a first order differential equation in Δn_2 and if ΔT is assumed to be constant, the equation is identical in form with equations 2.39 and 2.40.

Putting Δn_2 equal to zero where $t = 0$ and taking its final value as $n_2 k_{21} \Delta W \Delta T / (k_{12} + k_{21}) \kappa T^2$ the solution becomes:

$$\Delta n_2 = (n_2 k_{21} \tau \Delta W \Delta T / \kappa T^2) \{1 - \exp.(-t/\tau)\}$$

where τ is written in place of $1/(k_{12} + k_{21})$. By analogy with equation 2.42, τ is seen to be the relaxation time for the process. Assuming that Δn_2 varies sinusoidally with a frequency, $f = \omega/2\pi$, we have that:

$$\Delta n_2 = \frac{n_2 k_{21} \Delta W \Delta T}{\kappa T^2} \cdot \frac{\tau}{1 + j\omega\tau} \tag{4.35}$$

Now the first law of thermodynamics may be expressed as:

$$\Delta Q = \Delta U + P\Delta V,$$

where U represents the internal energy of the substance. For an ideal gas, U is a function of temperature only, so that for one mole:

$$\Delta U = C_v \Delta T,$$

where C_v is the molar heat at constant volume. ΔU consists of two parts:

(a) the contribution, $C_v^\infty \Delta T$, due to the translational energy of the molecules, C_v^∞ representing the value of C_v for $f = \infty$, i.e. at frequencies well above the relaxation frequency.

(b) the contribution, $n_2 \Delta W$, of the transfer energy to the excited state of the molecules, i.e.:

$$C_v = C_v^\infty + \Delta W \Delta n_2/\Delta T$$

or:

$$C_v = C_v^\infty + \frac{n_2 k_{21}(\Delta W)^2}{\kappa T^2} \frac{\tau}{1 + j\omega\tau} \tag{4.36}$$

At zero frequency, i.e.: $\omega = 0$, put $C_v = C_v^0$

Hence:

$$C_v^0 = C_v^\infty + C_i \tag{4.37}$$

where

$$C_i = n_2 k_{21}(\Delta W)^2 \tau/\kappa T^2 \tag{4.38}$$

Hence equation 4.36 may be expressed as:

$$C_v = C_v^\infty + \frac{C_i}{1 + j\omega\tau} \tag{4.39}$$

Put

$$C_p - C_v = D$$

where C_p represents the molar heat at constant pressure. For an ideal gas $D = R$, the universal gas constant. Hence, equations 4.36 to 4.39 inclusive may be rewritten with C_p substituted for C_v.

ABSORPTION IN GASES DUE TO THERMAL RELAXATION

Equation 2.29 shows that the velocity, v_ω, of sound at frequency, $\omega/2\pi$, is given by:

$$v_\omega^2 = \gamma \left(\frac{\partial P}{\partial \rho} \right)_T \qquad (4.40)$$

Since relaxational mechanisms depend only on temperature changes, one can assume that $(\partial P/\partial \rho)_T$ is independent of frequency. If we take c to represent the velocity of sound at 'zero' frequency, we have:

$$\frac{v_\omega^2}{c^2} = \frac{\gamma}{\gamma_0} \qquad (4.41)$$

where

i.e.
$$\gamma_0 = \frac{C_p^0}{C_v^0} \text{ and } \gamma = \frac{C_p}{C_v}$$

$$\frac{v_\omega^2}{c^2} = \frac{C_p}{C_v} \cdot \frac{C_v^0}{C_p^0} = \frac{C_v + D}{C_v} \cdot \frac{C_v^0}{C_p^0} \left(1 + \frac{D}{C_v} \right) \qquad (4.41a)$$

where
$$D = C_p - C_v = C_p^0 - C_v^0 = C_p^\infty - C_v^\infty \qquad (4.41a)$$

$$\text{Now} \frac{1}{C_v} = 1 \bigg/ \left(C_v^\infty + \frac{C_i}{1 + j\omega\tau} \right) = \frac{C_v^0 + \omega^2\tau^2 C_v^\infty + j\omega\tau C_i}{(C_v^0)^2 + \omega^2\tau^2(C_v^\infty)^2} \qquad (4.42)$$

i.e. v_ω is complex.

Now for propagation in the x-direction, equation 2.20c for the particle displacement, ξ, can be expressed as:

$$\xi = \xi_0 \exp. j\,(\omega t - kx) = \xi_0 \exp. j\omega\left(t - \frac{x}{v_\omega} \right)$$

Separating the exponential term into real and imaginary components one obtains the solution for damped harmonic vibrations, i.e. equation 2.38c viz.:

$$\xi = \xi_0 \exp. (-ax) \exp. j\omega \left(t - \frac{x}{v} \right)$$

where
$$\frac{1}{v_\omega} = \frac{1}{v}(1 - j\,av/\omega) \qquad (4.43)$$

i.e.:
$$\frac{v_\omega^2}{v^2} = \frac{1}{(1 - j\,av/\omega)^2} \simeq 1 + 2j\,av/\omega = 1 + jQ_m^{-1} \qquad (4.44)$$

where $Q_m^{-1} = a\lambda/\pi = 2av/\omega$ represents the loss per cycle (see equation 2.46a), assuming that $(av/\omega)^2 \ll 1$, which must be true if the waves are to travel any appreciable distance.

Hence from equations 4.41 and 4.42:

$$Q_m^{-1} = \frac{C_v^0}{C_p^0} \frac{\omega\tau C_i D}{(C_v^0)^2 + \omega^2\tau^2(C_v^\infty)^2} \qquad (4.45)$$

97

It can be easily shown by differentiating Q_m^{-1} with respect to ω and applying the usual conditions, that Q_m^{-1} is maximum when:

$$\omega_0 = \frac{1}{\tau}\frac{C_v^0}{C_v^\infty}$$

i.e. where $\omega = \omega_0 = 2\pi f_0$ f_0 being the *relaxation frequency*.

Hence:
$$Q_m^{-1} = \frac{C_i D}{C_p^0 C_v^\infty}\frac{\omega\omega_0}{\omega_0^2 + \omega^2} \tag{4.46}$$

and
$$\frac{v^2}{c^2} = \frac{C_v^0}{C_p^0}\left[1 + \frac{D}{C_v^\infty}\left(\frac{C_v^\infty}{C_v} + \frac{\omega^2}{\omega_0^2}\right)\Big/\left(1 + \frac{\omega^2}{\omega_0^2}\right)\right] \tag{4.47}$$

Substituting $\omega = \omega_0$ in equation 4.46 for which $Q_m^{-1} = Q_{max}^{-1}$ we have

$$Q_{max}^{-1} = \frac{1}{2}\frac{C_i}{C_p^0}\cdot\frac{D}{C_v^\infty} \tag{4.48}$$

or:
$$Q_{max}^{-1} = \frac{1}{2}\frac{\gamma_0 - 1}{\gamma_0}\frac{C_i}{C_v^\infty} \tag{4.48a}$$

From equation 4.48

$$Q_{max}^{-1} = \frac{D}{2\gamma_0}\frac{C_v^0 - C_v^\infty}{C_v^0 C_v^\infty} = \frac{1}{2\gamma_0}\left(\frac{C_p^\infty - C_v^\infty}{C_v^\infty} - \frac{C_p^0 - C_v^0}{C_v^0}\right)$$

$$= \frac{1}{2}\left(\frac{\gamma_\infty}{\gamma_0} - 1\right) \tag{4.48b}$$

By substituting 4.48 into equation 4.46, one obtains:

$$Q_m^{-1} = \frac{2\omega\omega_0}{\omega_0^2 + \omega^2}\,Q_{max}^{-1} \tag{4.49}$$

At frequencies such that $\omega \ll \omega_0$:

$$Q_m^{-1} = \frac{2\omega}{\omega_0}\,Q_{max}^{-1}$$

or:
$$Q_m^{-1} = \frac{\omega}{\omega_0}\frac{C_i}{C_p^0}\frac{D}{C_v^\infty} = \frac{\omega}{\omega_0}\frac{\gamma_0 - 1}{\gamma_0}\frac{C_i}{C_v^\infty}$$

or:
$$\alpha_{relax} = \frac{\omega Q_m^{-1}}{2v} \simeq \frac{\omega^2}{2\omega_0 c}\frac{C_i}{C_p^0}\frac{D}{C_v^\infty}$$

$$= \frac{\pi}{\omega_0 c}\cdot\frac{\gamma_0 - 1}{\gamma_0}\cdot\frac{C_i}{C_v^\infty}f^2 \tag{4.50b}$$

i.e.:
$$\alpha_{relax} \propto f^2$$

From equation 4.47 it is seen that for high frequencies $\omega \to \omega_\infty$ and $v \to v_\infty$

Thus:
$$\frac{v_\infty^2}{c^2} = \frac{\gamma_\infty}{\gamma_0} \tag{4.51}$$

i.e. velocity dispersion $= \dfrac{\Delta v}{c} = \dfrac{v_\infty - c}{c}$

$$= \left(\frac{\gamma_\infty}{\gamma_0} \right)^{\frac{1}{2}} - 1 \qquad (4.52)$$

But, from equation 4.48b:

$$\frac{\gamma_\infty}{\gamma_0} = 2Q_{max}^{-1} + 1$$

Hence:

$$\frac{\Delta v}{c} \backsimeq Q_{max}^{-1} \qquad (4.53)$$

for small values of dispersion.

The value of C_i may be determined from the Planck-Einstein equation:

$$C_i = R\left(\frac{h\nu}{\kappa T} \right)^2 \frac{\exp.(h\nu/\kappa T)}{\{\exp.(h\nu/\kappa T) - 1\}^2} \qquad (4.54)$$

Here ν represents the electromagnetic wave frequency, characteristic of the change of energy level for the given process, as given by $\Delta W = h\nu$, h being Planck's constant. ν may be obtained from spectroscopic observations.

4.6. VARIATIONS OF RELAXATION TIMES WITH PRESSURE AND TEMPERATURE

Because energy exchanges in a gas occur as a result of molecular collisions, it is reasonable to assume that a relaxation time for a given process is proportional to the average interval of time between these collisions and, hence, to the molecular mean free path. Simple kinetic theory for an ideal gas predicts that the pressure of a gas varies inversely with the molecular mean free path. Thus the relaxation time for an ideal gas should be inversely proportional to the pressure.

The variation of relaxation time with temperature for a thermal relaxation process is seen by substituting the value for k_{21} given by equation 4.32 into the definition of relaxation time introduced into equation 4.34. Thus we have:

$$\tau = \frac{1}{k_{12}\{1 + \exp.(\Delta W/\kappa T)\}} \qquad (4.55)$$

4.7. OBSERVATIONS OF ABSORPTION AND VELOCITY DISPERSION IN GASES

4.7.1. General Considerations

For a thorough investigation of attenuation and velocity dispersion in gases it is desirable to obtain values of absorption coefficients and velocities for a continuous range of frequencies in the neighbourhood of the absorption peaks. These peaks normally occur in the megacycle frequency range for which, in gases, crystal sources are used. In Section 4.10, where experimental methods are discussed, it is shown that the ultrasonic interferometer using a quartz crystal vibrating at resonance is the only instrument at present available for really satisfactory measurements in gases. With this device only the natural frequencies of the crystal source can be excited and a change of frequency is obtained only by changing the source, a process which is time consuming and which can be very inconvenient. One can, however, vary the pressure of the gas instead of the frequency; this variation has the advantage of being a continuous one.

It was shown in the previous section that, for an ideal gas, relaxation times vary inversely with pressure; hence relaxation frequencies should vary directly with pressure. Let the relaxation frequency be f_0 at normal atmospheric pressure, P_0, and f_0' at some other pressure, P_0'. We thus have:

$$\frac{f_0}{P_0} = \frac{f_0'}{P_0'}$$

or if pressure is expressed in atmospheres:

$$f_0 = f_0'/P_0'$$

Thus by plotting absorption against the parameter f/P a curve similar to the one shown in *Figure 2.5* is obtained (see *Figure 4.2*). The peak occurs at a value:

$$(f/P)_0 = f_0'/P_0' = f_0$$

In the absence of dispersion, velocity remains constant with pressure for an ideal gas (see Section 4.1). Hence a plot of velocity against f/P should result in a dispersion curve similar to the one shown in *Figure 2.5* (see *Figure 4.2*).

The results available from measurements in gases may not always be reliable because of the considerable experimental difficulties, as discussed in Section 4.11.2. However, a very large number of measurements have been made since 1928 and a definite pattern is indicated by them, as seen below.

4.7.2. Monatomic Gases

Measurements made on monatomic gases, after making due allowances for experimental inaccuracies, produce results which are in good agreement with those predicted by the classical theory of absorption.

4.7.3. Diatomic Gases

In diatomic gases, such as hydrogen, oxygen and nitrogen, only the rotational degrees of freedom of their molecules can be excited without difficulty at normal temperatures. This is because of their high characteristic temperatures (see Section 4.4) for vibrational degrees of freedom. Minimum values of Θ in hydrogen, oxygen and nitrogen are 5,958, 2,228, and 3,336° K respectively. One may thus expect that any values of Θ in excess of those predicted for such gases at normal temperatures are due to rotational relaxation.

Stewart and Stewart[2], using the apparatus described in Section 4.11.3, carried out a long series of measurements of velocity and attenuation for hydrogen at megacycle frequencies, at varying pressures between 1 and 0·5 atmosphere. At 25° C absorption was about twenty-five times greater than the classical value, which indicated a rotational relaxation time of 2×10^{-8} sec. A number of experimenters (see Herzfeld and Litovitz[3], p. 238) measured absorption coefficients in nitrogen and oxygen and obtained room temperature values for the ratio a/a_{class} of about 1·2, which corresponds to relaxation times of the order of 10^{-9} sec. The shorter relaxation times for nitrogen and oxygen compared with hydrogen are to be expected in view of the larger masses of their molecules.

4.7.4. Polyatomic Gases

For polyatomic gases the values of Θ characteristic of vibrational degrees of freedom are, in many instances, much lower than for diatomic gases. Consequently, absorption caused by vibrational relaxation may be observed at room temperatures for many such gases. A polyatomic molecule may have a number of different modes of vibration, which can result in the appearance of several corresponding relaxation times. This is evident from the appearance of peak structure or a broad relaxation peak. Because the relaxation times for rotational exchanges are generally much shorter than those for vibrational exchanges of energy the effects of rotational relaxation are not normally observed.

Carbon dioxide is often quoted as a classical example of a substance possessing vibrational relaxation. The CO_2 molecule is one of a class of linear triatomic molecules (see *Figure 4.1*) with which are associated four modes of vibration, each being a source of electromagnetic radiation. The first two are deformation modes (*Figure 4.1a*) which account for two degrees of freedom in the two perpendicular planes containing the undisturbed molecule. These are associated with an infra-red spectral line of wavelength 15μ for which the frequency, ν, is 2×10^{13} c/s. The other two are valence

101

modes, one being symmetrical (*Figure 4.1b*) giving rise to a wavelength of $7 \cdot 8\mu$ ($\nu = 3 \cdot 8 \times 10^{13}$ c/s) and the other asymmetrical (*Figure 4.1c*) for which there is a wavelength of $4 \cdot 3\mu$ ($\nu = 7 \times 10^{13}$ c/s). The corresponding values of Θ are 959, 1,920, and 3,380° K respectively. The symmetrical mode is optically inactive and it appears only in the Raman effect. In addition there is a vibration of frequency $4 \cdot 2 \times 10^{13}$ c/s ($\lambda = 7 \cdot 2\mu$) caused by resonance between the symmetrical valence mode and an overtone of the deformation mode. These values of frequency may be substituted into the Planck-Einstein equation 4.54 to obtain the contribution towards the value of C_i for each of the fundamental modes of vibration. Whether one is justified in considering values of C_i individually for each mode of vibration and thus produce a separate relaxation time for each degree of freedom or to add together all of these values of C_i to obtain only one relaxation time is a controversial question.

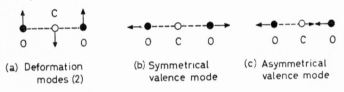

(a) Deformation modes (2)   (b) Symmetrical valence mode   (c) Asymmetrical valence mode

Figure 4.1. Fundamental modes of vibration of CO_2 molecule

Relaxation in CO_2 was first detected in 1925 by Pierce, who observed velocity dispersion. Abello first reported excess absorption in this gas in 1927, and since then a large number of observations of attenuation and velocity dispersion have been made. Room temperature measurements have indicated that vibrational relaxation times for CO_2 are of the order of more than 10^{-6} sec. Most experimenters have found only one vibrational relaxation time but a number claim to have detected the presence of two. For example, Buschmann and Schäfer[3], from measurements of velocity dispersion, obtained values of relaxation times of $1 \cdot 53 \times 10^{-6}$ and $6 \cdot 9 \times 10^{-6}$ sec, both at 21° C. These were attributed to the deformation and symmetrical valence modes, respectively. On the other hand, by means of an infra-red method, Slobodskaya[3] observed similar relaxation times which he ascribed to the deformation and asymmetrical valence modes; it was not possible to excite the symmetrical valence mode optically.

COS, CS_2 and N_2O are other examples of linear triatomic molecules. For each of these, vibrational relaxation times of the same order as for CO_2 have been determined. *Figure 4.2* illustrates velocity dispersion and absorption curves for CS_2 vapour. The theoretical curves assume a single vibrational relaxation time.

For non-linear triatomic molecules, i.e. those with atoms at the apices of triangles, the vibrational relaxation times are shorter than for linear triatomic molecules. Values of about 3×10^{-8} sec for H_2O at $300°$ C and 2 to 3×10^{-7} sec for SO_2 at $20°$ C have been obtained. For larger molecules, measured values of relaxation times have been found to vary between 10^{-9} and about 10^{-6} sec. They include, approximately, 3×10^{-9} sec (C_2H_6 at $14°$ C), $8 \cdot 3 \times 10^{-8}$ sec (CCl_4 at $100°$ C), $1 \cdot 5 \times 10^{-7}$ sec (C_6H_6 at $96°$ C), and 3×10^{-6} sec (CH_3F at $100°$ C).

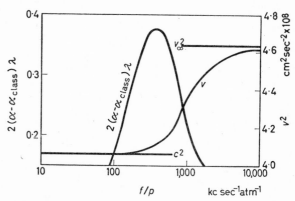

Figure 4.2. Theoretical absorption and dispersion curves for CS_2 vapour (after Richards and Reid[9] and Angona[10]). (Experimental results obtained by these workers were in good agreement with these curves)

4.8. MIXTURES OF GASES

Observations on mixtures of two gases not reacting chemically with one another have shown that the velocity of sound varies linearly with concentration between limiting values, which are the velocities for the two components in their pure states. On the other hand, this linear relationship does not apply to attenuation, because of the effect on relaxation times by changing the mixture concentration.

The relaxation time, τ, for a given cause of absorption may be expressed by the relationship:

$$\tau = Z\tau_c$$

where τ_c represents the mean time elapsing between successive collisions and Z, the average number of collisions required to effect the particular exchange of energy. The value of τ_c is obtained purely from considerations of simple kinetic theory but Z depends upon the efficiency of the energy transfer for each collision. The higher the value of Z, the less efficient is the energy exchange and there is thus a longer relaxation time.

Consider, for example, carbon dioxide at room temperature for which values of τ and Z for vibrational energy exchanges are of the order of 10^{-5} sec and 50,000, respectively, and water vapour also at

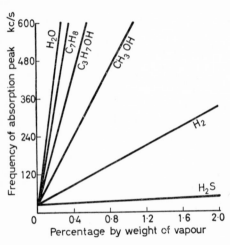

Figure 4.3. Variation of frequency of absorption peak with concentration for various impurities in carbon dioxide (after Knudsen and Fricke[11])

room temperature for which the corresponding values of τ and Z are about 3×10^{-8} sec and 300, respectively. The introduction of water vapour into pure carbon dioxide will have the effect of increasing the efficiency of energy transfer on collision and thus to reduce the relaxation time. *Figure 4.3* illustrates the effect on the relaxation frequency of CO_2 by the introduction of small quantities of various impurities. It is seen that the addition of 1 per cent by weight of water vapour to pure carbon dioxide increases the vibrational relaxation frequency from about 15 kc/s to over 2 Mc/s. Thus if ultrasonic waves at a frequency of 1 Mc/s are propagated through pure carbon dioxide, absorption due to vibrational relaxation is small since Q_{max}^{-1} will be well beyond the relaxation peak of *Figure 2.5*. On the other hand, if waves of this frequency are passed through carbon dioxide containing 1 per cent water vapour attenuation will be very high because the operating point is close to the highest point on the peak. This illustrates the importance (see Section 4.11.2(ii)) of excluding the smallest trace of impurity from gases for absorption measurements.

4.9. CHEMICAL REACTIONS

It was shown as early as 1920 by Einstein that chemical reactions may give rise to acoustic relaxation. He suggested that velocity dispersion measurements be used to study the dissociation of nitrogen tetroxide, i.e. $N_2O_4 \rightleftarrows 2NO_2$, and this was investigated experimentally by Richards and Reid.[4] It is believed that the relaxation results from the displacement of a chemical equilibrium by the sound wave, but it is difficult to separate the results of this effect from those of thermal relaxation. A discussion of this phenomenon in gases and liquids will be found in Herzfeld and Litovitz.[3]

4.10. MEASUREMENTS IN GASES

Gases are characterized by the following properties:

(i) Low characteristic impedances compared with those for solids; thus only a small fraction of the energy from the transducer is transmitted into the medium.

(ii) Relatively high absorption coefficients which usually increase with the square of the frequency. At megacycle frequencies the effective path length may be only a few wavelengths.

(iii) Lower velocities, in general, than in liquids and solids; e.g. room temperature values of longitudinal wave velocities in air, water, and steel are about 340, 1,500, and 6,000 metres sec^{-1}, respectively.

Possible ways of measuring propagation constants in gases include the *optical diffraction method* (see Section 5.11), the *reverberation method* (see Section 5.12), the *pulse technique* (see Sections 5.10 and 6.11), and the *acoustic interferometer*. Because of the poor degree of coupling between the source and medium, best results are obtained with methods which involve resonance of the medium; for this the acoustic interferometer is the most satisfactory one. This instrument, to be described below, is capable of a high degree of precision provided that the stringent requirements for its design are met with.

The optical diffraction method has not proved successful for gases, except perhaps at very high pressures. This is because of the very small changes in density and, hence, refractive index brought about by the passage of the sound waves. Some degree of success has been achieved by Tempest and Parbrook[15] at megacycle frequencies but difficulties with this method usually arise because of the high attenuation in gases at such frequencies. This factor also limits the use of the reverberation method because the reverberation time for the container is usually very much higher than that for the gas, except at low frequencies. Edmonds and Lamb,[16] however, designed an instrument in which reverberation occurred at a resonant frequency for gas in the container. Successful results were obtained for triatomic gases at frequencies up to 25 kc/s.

4.11. THE ACOUSTIC INTERFEROMETER

4.11.1 General Considerations

For the acoustic interferometer stationary waves are produced in a gas column and the effects of varying the acoustic path length are investigated. The instrument consists essentially of a reversible transducer at one end of the column and, at the other end, a plane parallel reflector which can be moved either towards or away from

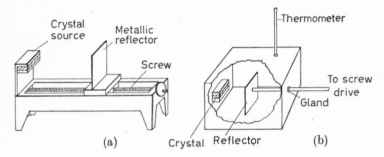

Figure 4.4. Pierce's interferometer

(a) Arrangement of crystal and reflector for measurements in air
(b) Arrangement of crystal and reflector for measurements in gases

the transducer. For investigations at megacycle frequencies a quartz crystal is normally used and this forms a second reflecting surface. The pressure variation in the gas column for different values of the distance of separation between the transducer and reflector is expressed by equation 2.66. *Figure 4.4* shows an early form of ultrasonic interferometer as used for gases, designed by Pierce (1925). The source was a quartz crystal which was excited by a circuit similar to that shown in *Figure 3.2*. The metal reflector was moved relative to and kept parallel with the crystal surface by means of a micrometer screw drive. To avoid any capacitance between the radiating crystal surface and the reflector, both were maintained at earth potential.

The anode current was measured as a function of the position of the reflector and the variation was seen to be periodic (see *Figure 4.5*). Maximum values of current, which corresponded to resonance, were observed at half-wavelength intervals. Using the value of wavelength obtained from measurements of peak separation distance and the value of the crystal frequency as measured by a wavemeter, the velocity in the gas was calculated.

Measurements were made at frequencies ranging from 40 kc/s to 1·5 Mc/s for atmospheric air with the apparatus shown in *Figure 4.4a* and for carbon dioxide with the arrangement in *Figure 4.4b*.

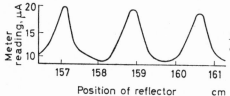

Figure 4.5. Variation of anode current with reflector position for Pierce's interferometer

Velocity dispersion was detected in carbon dioxide at frequencies between 40 kc/s and 200 kc/s. Attempts were made to measure absorption coefficients from observations of the decrements of the peak heights but there was an insufficient degree of accuracy consistent with reliable results.

One is not justified in using Pierce's method for measuring absorption coefficients because the structure of the peaks shown in *Figure 4.5* depends also on the characteristics of the circuit of the oscillator which excites the crystal. A technique for obtaining accurate values of absorption coefficients with the acoustic interferometer was devised by Hubbard in 1931. He considered the equivalent electrical circuits of the electronic oscillator, the crystal,

Figure 4.6. Hubbard's arrangement of exciting circuit and crystal

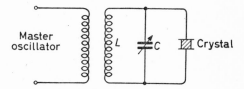

the gas column, and the reflector as being a single system. The oscillator was loosely coupled to an *LC* circuit with the quartz crystal shunted across the capacitor (see *Figure 4.6*). The oscillator and *LC* circuit were accurately tuned to the crystal frequency and the current through the crystal measured by a thermogalvanometer, resonance being indicated by minimum crystal current. The curve showing the variation of current with reflector distance was similar in form to that given in *Figure 2.8a*. Values of wavelength were obtained directly from the distances between the peaks. Absorption coefficients were calculated by a complicated process which involved measuring the peak heights and their widths. For gases having low attenuation, values of absorption coefficients could be obtained directly from the decrements of the peak heights, their widths being negligible.

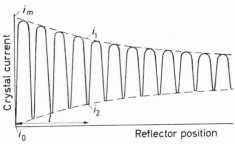

(a) Variation of crystal current with reflector position

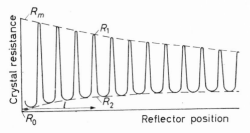

(b) Variation of crystal resistance with reflector position

Figure 4.7. Borgnis' modification of Hubbard's curves for a gas-filled ultrasonic interferometer (after Mason[5]) (N.B. For liquids the corresponding curves are inverted)

Hubbard's method may be simplified (see Mason[5], p. 315) by shunting out the electrical capacitance of the transducer with an inductance. The absorption coefficient, a, is then obtained only from the peak heights (see *Figure 4.7a*) using the equation:

$$\tanh al = \left\{ \frac{(\sigma_1 - 1)(\sigma_0 - \sigma_2)}{(\sigma_0 - 1)(\sigma_2 - 1)} \right\}^{\frac{1}{2}} \tag{4.56}$$

Here: $\sigma_0 = i_m/i_0, \ \sigma_1 = i_m/i_1, \text{ and } \sigma_2 = i_m/i_2$

108

where i_m and i_0 are the respective maximum and minimum values of the crystal current, obtained by extrapolating the peak envelopes back to zero separation of source and reflector. i_1 and i_2 are the respective maximum and minimum values of crystal current as represented by the envelopes at a peak position for a distance, l, of separation of source and reflector. Alternatively, one can measure crystal resistance instead of current and obtain the peaks shown in *Figure 4.7b*. The value of a is then given by the expression:

$$\tanh\ al = \left\{ \frac{(R_m - R_0)\,(R_2 - R_0)}{(R_1 - R_0)\,(R_m - R_1)} \right\}^{\frac{1}{2}} \tag{4.57}$$

where R represents the crystal resistance and the suffixes have the same meanings as before. The author has found that, in practice, the difference between i_m and i_1 and hence that between σ_1 and 1 can be very small, so that even with the use of a highly sensitive galvanometer the degree of accuracy of measuring a may not be high.

Crystal currents may be recorded automatically by obtaining the readings of the thermogalvanometer on a chart placed on a revolving drum. The reflector is moved slowly by an accurate screw which is turned by a suitably geared down constant speed electric motor, the motion of which is synchronized with the rotation of the drum. Care must be taken that vibrations of the motor are not communicated to either the reflector or to the recording mechanism.

A more direct method of determining absorption coefficients, which is suitable only for lower frequencies, is to adjust the reflector to a position for resonance of the gas column and to explore the stationary wave configuration with a probe microphone. The pressure amplitude variation in the sound field is given by equation 2.65b remembering that, for resonance, $l = n\lambda/2$ or $kl = n\pi$. The position for maximum pressure amplitude, p_{max}, is given by $x = n\lambda/2$ or $kx = n\pi$ and that for minimum pressure amplitude, p_{min}, by $x = (2n+1)\lambda/4$ or $kx = (2n+1)\pi/2$. Substituting these conditions into this equation gives:

$$p_{max} = \frac{\cosh\ a(l-x)}{\sinh\ al}$$

$$p_{min} = \frac{\sinh\ a(l-x)}{\sinh\ al}$$

so that the standing wave ratio, SWR, is given by the expression:

$$SWR = \frac{p_{max}}{p_{min}} = \coth\ a(l-x)$$

Richardson and others[6] used a hot-wire microphone as a detector for measurements in vapours having long relaxation times at frequencies of up to 400 kc/s.

4.11.2. Experimental Difficulties

Great care must be taken with the design of the acoustic interferometer if the measured values of attenuation are to be of any use. Furthermore, attention must be paid to maintaining steady physical conditions. Difficulties are due mainly to:

(i) irregularities in peak structure;

(ii) the presence of impurities in the medium.

(i) *Irregularities in peak structure*

These may occur for the following reasons:

(a) the surfaces of both source and reflector not being rigorously plane parallel with one another;

(b) irregularities in the vibrations of the source;

(c) diffraction;

(d) the 'waveguide' effect.

Lack of parallelism of source and reflector results in the acoustic path length not being constant for all rays in the beam. This leads to the broadening and lowering of the peaks together with the possible appearance of fine structure, thus resulting in too high a value of attenuation. Parallelism should be correct to within a wavelength or two of light.

Irregularities in the vibrations of the source, which give rise to lack of frequency stability, may be prevented by the correct mounting of the transducer crystal (see Section 4.11.3) and also by ensuring that the input current does not overload the crystal. Overloading may cause the generation of unwanted harmonics.

Diffraction effects can be avoided by arranging that the whole of the sound field under consideration lies within the Fresnel zone (see Section 2.12) so that the acoustic intensity will have died down to below a measurable quantity at a distance of less than a^2/λ from the source, where a represents the radius of the transducer surface. Failure to ensure this will result in energy being diverted from the main part of the beam so that an exaggerated value of a will be obtained. Worse still, the diffracted rays may be reflected from the walls of the interferometer and interfere with the main beam.

The waveguide effect, which produces Rayleigh cross modes, has been described in Section 2.13. It can be caused by non-piston like vibrations of the source due to incorrect mounting and results in the appearance of satellite peaks.

(ii) *The presence of impurities in the medium*

It was shown in Section 4.8 that the addition of impurities, even in negligible quantities, to a gas could have a considerable effect on its relaxation times. The measured value of absorption would then be completely different from that for the gas in its pure form. Three ways in which impurities can be introduced into a gas in an interferometer are:

(a) the gas as supplied may not be 100 per cent pure,

(b) the materials from which the interferometer is made may contaminate the gas, and

(c) leakage into the interferometer chamber may take place during measurements.

Great care must be taken in purifying the gas, for which a gas-handling system such as that devised by Thaler[12] (see *Figure 4.8*) should be used. Contamination may arise from corrosion by the gas of a metal part, vacuum grease used for sealing the apparatus, or

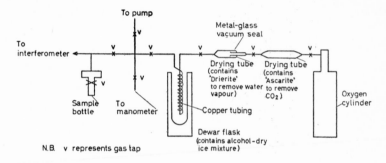

Figure 4.8. Gas-handling system used by Thaler[12]

mercury vapour from the pressure gauge. This difficulty can be overcome only by a proper choice of materials (e.g. the use of very low vapour pressure vacuum grease) and the proper design of the apparatus (e.g. the inclusion of mercury vapour traps).

The danger of contamination by leakage is always present, the greatest source being gaps between moving parts. Pierce (see *Figure 4.4b*) used a packing gland as a seal between the moving reflector rod and the walls of the chamber. This type of seal does not provide an efficient gas-tight arrangement, especially at low pressures, and the packing-gland itself might provide a source of impurity. Stewart[7] resolved this difficulty by completely enclosing all moving parts within the gas-tight container (see the following sub-section).

4.11.3. Experimental Techniques

Stewart's[7] apparatus (see *Figure 4.9*) consists of a double bellows, B, enclosing all moving parts. This arrangement ensures that the volume and, hence, the pressure of the gas remain constant whilst the reflector is being moved. The outer ends of the bellows are soldered to the caps, C, to form gas-tight joints. The caps are connected to three guide-bars, G, and the bottom cap is securely screwed to the base of the brass piston, P, the top surface of which

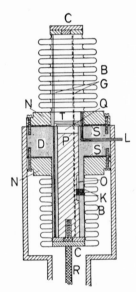

Figure 4.9. Stewart's interferometer[7]

forms the reflector. In order to maintain parallelism between the source and reflector, the piston is made to fit closely into the brass cylinder, D. The caps, C, the guide bars, G, and the piston, P, form a rigid framework, so that the volume enclosed by the chamber is constant for all positions of the reflector. The inner ends of the bellows are soldered to the steel rings, N, to form gas-tight connections. These rings are then tightly screwed to the cylinder, D, gas-tight temperature-resistant seals being obtained by means of the copper gaskets, S. In this manner the chamber may be opened and resealed for adjustments to the crystal, etc., without any trouble whilst the nature of the gas-tight seals remains unaltered. The long quartz rod, R, having a negligible coefficient of expansion, connects the piston to a micrometer screw gauge. The bellows also serve the purpose of supplying a restoring force which keeps the motion of the reflector closely following that of the micrometer screw. L is a copper exhaust tube for the gas and it also carries a coaxial conducting lead, which is surrounded by a 2-mm Pyrex glass tube. Q is the quartz crystal source and T is the backing plate, a quarter-wavelength from it. When the instrument was constructed, the piston and cylinder were machined to a tight fit and then polished together, whilst the piston was securely clamped by a long screw fitting into the keyhole at K. The common surface was ground to an optical flatness. The screw was then removed and replaced by a

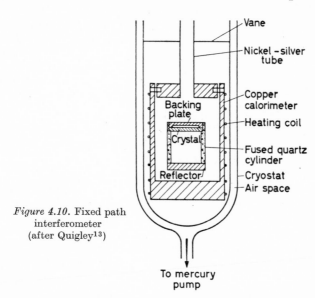

Figure 4.10. Fixed path
interferometer
(after Quigley[13])

To mercury
pump

blunt key which fitted into the slot, O, so that the piston would not rotate when moved. With the crystal resting on the top surface of the cylinder, its lower surface was shown to be plane parallel to the reflecting end of the piston to within one or two optical fringes. With this type of instrument it is possible to measure wavelengths to about one micron, the limit of accuracy of the micrometer, and absorption coefficients to an accuracy of better than one per cent.

The difficulty of enclosing all moving parts can also be overcome by using a fixed-path interferometer, i.e. in which all moving parts are eliminated (see *Figure 4.10*). This has been used for measuring variations of propagation constants with temperature or pressure. The distance between the source and reflector is altered by changing temperature or pressure, instead of path length.

Because the ultrasonic interferometer works under conditions of resonance it is necessary to use a transducer having a high Q factor and to mount it so that damping is at a minimum. Theoretically, best results occur with nodal mountings (see *Figure 4.11*) but for a crystal source having a thickness of less than one millimetre a considerable amount of skill is required to obtain such a mounting since it is necessary to cut a nodal groove or work a bevel around the edge of the plate. Furthermore, one must still make contact with the electrodes to provide a path for the crystal current. This difficulty has

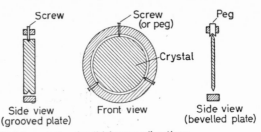

(a) Nodal mounting for thickness vibrations

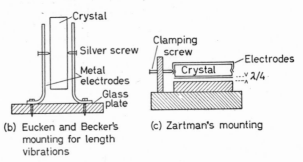

(b) Eucken and Becker's mounting for length vibrations

(c) Zartman's mounting

Figure 4.11. Nodal mountings for transducer crystals

been overcome by an ingenious method due to Zartman[8] (*Figure 4.11c*). The coating which provides the electrode on the upper surface is extended over the edge to the nodal groove, so that the three supporting pins are in electrical contact with it. In this way the upper electrode is kept at earth potential. The other connection is made by capacity coupling between the lower surface and a parallel metal plate, which also provides quarter-wavelength backing (see Sections 2.11.2 and 3.4).

A less satisfactory but often more practical alternative to nodal mounting is to rest the plated crystal on a horizontal metal platform, to which the 'live' lead is connected, and to use a spring contact with the upper surface to provide the earth lead. The spring

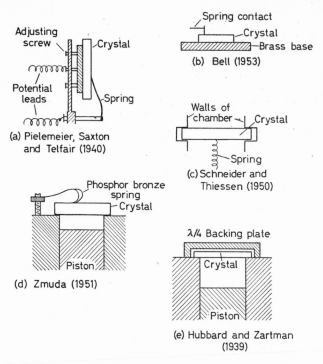

Figure 4.12. Platform-type crystal mountings

should be sufficiently stiff to maintain unbroken electrical contact during the vibrations but not to damp the vibrations to any appreciable extent. This and other types of crystal mountings are shown in *Figure 4.12*.

REFERENCES

1. ROBERTS, J. K. and MILLER, A. R. *Heat and Thermodynamics*, 5th Edn., London, 1960
2. STEWART, E. S. and STEWART, J. L. *J. acoust. Soc. Amer.*, 1952, **24**, 194
3. HERZFELD, K. F. and LITOVITZ, T. A. *Absorption and Dispersion of Ultrasonics*, Academic Press, New York, 1959
4. RICHARDS, W. T. and REID, J. A. *J. Chem. Phys.*, 1933, **1**, 114

5. MASON, W. P. *Piezoelectric Crystals and their Application to Ultrasonics*, van Nostrand, New York, 1950 ·
6. RICHARDSON, E. G. *Ultrasonic Physics*, 2nd Edn., Elsevier, Amsterdam, 1962
7. STEWART, J. L. *Rev. sci. Instrum.*, 1946, **17**, 59
8. ZARTMAN, I. F. *J. acoust. Soc. Amer.*, 1949, **21**, 171
9. RICHARDS, W. T. and REID, J. A. *J. chem. Phys.*, 1934, **2**, 193
10. ANGONA, F. A. *J. acoust. Soc. Amer.*, 1954, **25**, 1116
11. KNUDSEN, V. O. and FRICKE, E. *J. acoust. Soc. Amer.*, 1940, **12**, 255
12. THALER, W. J. *J. acoust. Soc. Amer.*, 1953, **24**, 15
13. QUIGLEY, T. H. *Phys. Rev.*, 1945, **67**, 298
14. KAYE, G. W. C. and LABY, T. H. *Tables of Physical and Chemical Constants*, 11th Edn., Longmans, Green, London, 1957
15. TEMPEST, W. and PARBROOK, H. D. *Acustica*, 1957, **7**, 356
16. EDMONDS, P. D. and LAMB, J. *Proc. Phys. Soc.*, 1958, **71**, 17

LOW AMPLITUDE PROPAGATION IN LIQUIDS

5.1. VELOCITIES IN LIQUIDS

WITH certain exceptions which are discussed in Section 5.5, liquids, in common with gases, do not support shear stresses and, for this reason, only longitudinal waves can be passed through them. The speed of sound in a liquid may be obtained from equation 2.26 by replacing E by the adiabatic bulk modulus K_S, as follows:

$$c = (K_s/\rho)^{\frac{1}{2}} \tag{5.1}$$

Values of c for a number of liquids at normal temperatures are listed in *Table 5.1*.

Table 5.1. Calculated Values of Acoustic Velocities and Viscous Relaxation Characteristics for Liquids at 20° C

The values of τ_{vis} and a_{vis}/f^2 listed below have been calculated from data given by Kaye and Laby[20] using equations 4.11 and 4.12

Liquid	Velocity c m sec^{-1}	Viscous Relaxation time τ_{vis} sec	Viscous absorption a_{vis}/f^2 neper cm^{-1} sec^2
Acetone	1,200	3.8×10^{-13}	6.3×10^{-17}
Benzene	1,320	5.6×10^{-13}	8.4×10^{-17}
Carbon tetrachloride	950	9.2×10^{-13}	2.0×10^{-16}
Castor oil	1,500	6.2×10^{-10}	8.1×10^{-14}
Chlorobenzene	1,320	6.8×10^{-13}	1.0×10^{-16}
Ethyl alcohol	1,200	1.7×10^{-12}	2.9×10^{-16}
Glycerol (pure)	1,940	4.2×10^{-10}	5.7×10^{-14}
Methyl alcohol	1,120	7.9×10^{-13}	1.4×10^{-16}
Nitrobenzene	1,480	1.1×10^{-12}	1.4×10^{-16}
Olive oil	1,440	6.0×10^{-11}	8.2×10^{-15}
Toluene	1,320	5.2×10^{-13}	7.7×10^{-17}
Water	1,490	6.0×10^{-13}	8.0×10^{-17}

The variation of the speed of sound with temperature in a liquid may be obtained in the following manner. It can be shown, see for example Roberts and Miller[1] (p. 335), that for unit mass of substance:

$$c_p - c_v = -T \left(\frac{\partial P}{\partial V} \right)_T \left(\frac{\partial V}{\partial T} \right)_P^2$$

Here c_p and c_v represent specific heats at constant pressure and temperature, respectively, T the absolute temperature, P the pressure, and V the volume. Now the isothermal bulk modulus K_T is given by:

$$K_T = K_S / \gamma = -\frac{1}{V} \left(\frac{\partial P}{\partial V} \right)_T$$

and the coefficient of expansion, a_p, at constant pressure by:

$$a_p = \frac{1}{V} \left(\frac{\partial V}{\partial T} \right)_P$$

Hence: $\qquad c_p - c_v = T a_p^2 K_S / \gamma P = T a_p^2 C^2 / \gamma$

from which it can be seen that:

$$c = \{ c_p (\gamma - 1) / a_p^2 T \}^{\frac{1}{2}} \qquad (5.2)$$

Equation 5.2 shows that, provided the quantities c_p, γ, and a_p remain sensibly constant, the speed of sound in a liquid decreases when the temperature is increased. This has been found to be true for most pure liquids at temperatures far enough removed from the critical temperature. For water under normal conditions, c_p, γ, and a_p vary considerably with temperature, and it has been found experimentally that the speed of sound in water increases with temperature until a maximum is reached at 73° C. Beyond this there is a decrease of velocity with temperature rise.

5.2. ABSORPTION AND VELOCITY DISPERSION IN LIQUIDS

5.2.1. General Considerations

The equations 4.12 and 4.26, which predict attenuation in gases due to viscosity and thermal conduction, respectively, apply also to liquids. This has been confirmed experimentally by measurements in monatomic liquids, such as mercury and liquid argon, and also in nitrogen, oxygen, and hydrogen in their liquid states, for which the temperatures are too low to excite any of the internal degrees of freedom of their molecules. An inspection of equation 4.27 reveals that the ratio, a_{th} / a_{vis} is in general very small and, except perhaps for liquid metals, thermal conduction plays a negligible part towards ultrasonic attenuation. Relaxation times for viscosity and thermal conduction for liquids are much shorter than for gases and the corresponding absorption coefficients are much lower. For viscosity, relaxation times are of the order of 10^{-12} sec and values of a/f^2 are of the order of 10^{-16} neper cm^{-1} sec^2 (see *Table 5.1*). Relaxation times for thermal conduction are in the region of 10^{-17} sec and the corresponding values of a/f^2 are of the order of 10^{-20} neper cm^{-1} sec^2. In general one can regard the attenuation due to thermal conduction as negligible compared with that due to viscosity.

Attenuation in excess of the classical values occurs in polyatomic liquids as well as in polyatomic gases. In many cases thermal relaxation can account for this but in associated liquids, such as water and the alcohols, structural relaxation has been shown to be a cause of absorption.

5.2.2. *Thermal Relaxation in Liquids*

Thermal relaxations of two different kinds have been shown to occur for liquids. The first of these is characterized by very short relaxation times of the order of 10^{-10} sec or less and the other by much longer relaxation times which may be greater than 10^{-6} sec.

It has been found that the mechanism associated with the shorter relaxation time is vibrational relaxation; for example, Andrea, Heasall and Lamb[2] have conducted experiments on liquid carbon disulphide (CS_2), the molecules of which have three vibrational degrees of freedom at room temperatures. By assuming that the value of absorption in excess of its 'classical' value was accounted for only by vibrational relaxation, they calculated the values of C_i; these were found to agree with the values obtained from spectroscopic observations.

Because of the very short relaxation times for liquids, the determination of their values by absorption measurements have not proved very fruitful except for a few liquids such as carbon disulphide. This is because of the high acoustic frequencies which would be required. However, hypersonic methods (see Section 5.14) have been used to measure velocity dispersion, but there has been some uncertainty as to the reliability of the values of relaxation times obtained in this way. The reason for this is that one is not sure whether or not all of the degrees of freedom have relaxed at the upper frequency limit. However, the results for carbon disulphide from these measurements have agreed with those obtained from attenuation measurements.

Karpovich[3] has demonstrated that there is another form of thermal relaxation, for which there are longer relaxation times. This is caused by the motion of rotational isomers. Certain substances, such as ethyl acetate and cyclohexane, may exist in two forms at different energy levels. Cyclohexane, for example, can exist in either the 'Pseudochair' or 'Boat' forms (see *Figure 5.1*) and relaxation between these forms may be brought about by sound waves. Karpovich obtained a series of values of isomeric relaxation frequencies ranging from 80 kc/s at 36° C for cyclohexane to 11·8 Mc/s at 20° C for ethyl acetate.

5.2.3. Structural Relaxation in Liquids

Equation 4.55 indicates a variation of thermal relaxation time and, hence, absorption with temperature, because of thermal relaxation. Fox and Rock in 1946 conducted measurements in water over a temperature range, 2 to 40° C and found an excess of attenuation

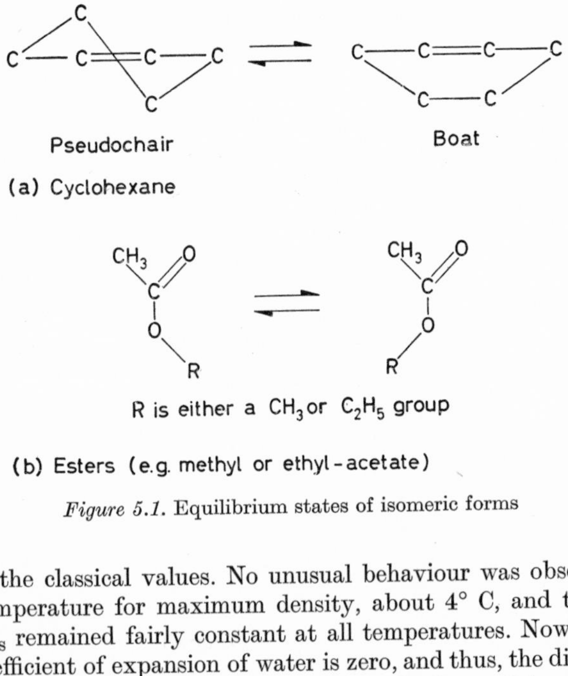

(a) Cyclohexane

    Pseudochair   Boat

R is either a CH_3 or C_2H_5 group

(b) Esters (e.g. methyl or ethyl-acetate)

Figure 5.1. Equilibrium states of isomeric forms

above the classical values. No unusual behaviour was observed at the temperature for maximum density, about 4° C, and the ratio a/a_{class} remained fairly constant at all temperatures. Now at 4° C the coefficient of expansion of water is zero, and thus, the difference, $C_p - C_v$, between its principal molar heats, the factor D in equations 4.45 and 4.50, must also be zero. Hence any excess absorption observed for water must be caused by a phenomenon other than thermal relaxation.

This excess absorption has been shown to be caused by structural or volume relaxation. It occurs in associated liquids such as water, the alcohols, glycerol, and polymeric liquids in which there are relatively large intermolecular forces. It can be explained by postulating a bulk or compressional viscosity which bears the same relationship to compressional stress as shear viscosity to shear stress. The relaxation times corresponding to this phenomenon are much shorter than those associated with thermal relaxation.

A liquid, when at rest, has a lattice structure similar to that possessed by a solid (see Section 6.1). When sound waves are propagated through a liquid, the resultant periodic changes of pressure cause molecules to flow into vacancies in the lattice during the compression phase and to return to their original positions in the lattice during the rarefaction portion of the cycle. Because a finite time is involved, the process is clearly a relaxational one. Changes of temperature which may occur do not affect this phenomenon.

Structural relaxation can be treated theoretically in the same way as thermal relaxation. By considering compressibility, β, which is the reciprocal of bulk modulus, instead of specific heat one can obtain an expression analogous to equation 4.39 i.e.:

$$\beta = \beta_\infty + \frac{\beta_r}{1 + j\omega\tau} \tag{5.3}$$

and hence:

$$\beta_0 = \beta_\infty + \beta_r \tag{5.4}$$

where τ represents the relaxation time and β_r the contribution to β caused by the relaxational effect. The subscripts 0 and ∞ refer to zero and infinite frequency, respectively. Proceeding as in Section 4.5, we have:

$$v_\omega^2 = v^2 (1 + jQ_m^{-1}) \qquad \text{(i.e. equation 4.44)}$$

where v is the velocity and Q_m^{-1}, the loss per cycle.

Putting: $v_\omega^2 = 1/\beta\rho$ we have

$$v^2 = \frac{\beta_0 + \beta_\infty\omega^2\tau^2}{\rho(\beta_0^2 + \beta_\infty^2\omega^2\tau^2)} \tag{5.5}$$

and:

$$Q_m^{-1} = \frac{\omega\tau}{\rho v^2} \frac{\beta_r}{(\beta_0^2 + \beta_\infty^2\omega^2\tau^2)} = \frac{\omega\tau\beta_r}{\beta_0 + \beta_\infty\omega^2\tau^2} \tag{5.6}$$

as before, the maximum value of Q_m^{-1} occurs at the frequency, $f_0 = \omega_0/2\pi$, so that:

$$\omega_0^2\tau^2 = \frac{\beta_0}{\beta_\infty}$$

Hence:

$$Q_m^{-1} = \frac{\beta_r}{(\beta_0\beta_\infty)^{\frac{1}{2}}} \cdot \frac{\omega\omega_0}{\omega_0^2 + \omega^2} \tag{5.7}$$

121

For frequencies where $\omega \ll \omega_0$ one can write:

$$a_{relax} = \frac{\pi Q_m^{-1}}{\lambda} = \frac{\pi \beta_r}{cf_0(\beta_0\beta_\infty)^{\frac{1}{2}}}f^2 \qquad (5.8)$$

and from equation 5.5 we have

$$\frac{c^2}{v_\infty^2} = \frac{\beta_\infty}{\beta_0} \qquad (5.9)$$

The significance of β_0, β_∞, and β_r can be realized if one considers their analogy with the specific heats for thermal relaxation for which it is assumed that the liquid can exist in two energy states (1) and (2), having values, W_1 and W_2, respectively. For the lower state, W_1, the volume is larger (i.e. sparser packing) than for the higher state,

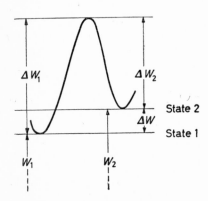

Figure 5.2. Potential diagram representing the energy states for water molecules in accordance with Hall's hypothesis

W_2. Here β_r represents the compressibility for the higher state. At lower frequencies where there is sufficient time for a complete transfer of energy from state 1 to state 2, β_r will be equal in value to β_0. β_∞ is the compressibility which corresponds to the lower state. At very high frequencies, where there is no time for any energy to flow from state 1 to state 2, β is equal in value to β_0. Hall[4] considered that (1) and (2) were states of equilibrium separated by a potential barrier (see *Figure 5.2*). He suggested that they were represented respectively by the liquid and glassy conditions of the substance at the same temperature. For water at 0° C these are liquid water (state 2) and ice (state 1). Values of β_0 and β_∞ may be obtained by velocity measurements.

The relaxation time, τ, is again given by:

$$\tau = 1/(k_{12} + k_{21})$$

where k_{12} and k_{21}, the average rates of flow of energy per molecule can be expressed as:

and:
$$k_{12} = (\kappa T/h) \exp.(-\Delta W_1/\kappa T)$$
$$k_{21} = (\kappa T/h) \exp.(-\Delta W_2/\kappa T)$$

so that:
$$\tau = (h/\kappa T)\frac{\exp.(\Delta W_1/\kappa T)}{1 + \exp.(\Delta W/\kappa T)} \qquad (5.10a)$$

or:
$$= (h/\kappa T)\frac{\exp.(\Delta W_2/\kappa T)}{1 + \exp.(-\Delta W/\kappa T)} \qquad (5.10b)$$

where $\Delta W = W_2 - W_1$, and ΔW_1 and ΔW_2 are the respective distances of the levels, W_1 and W_2, below the potential barrier. As before, T represents the absolute temperature, κ, Boltzmann's constant, and h, Planck's constant.

Hall assumed that the activation energy for the barrier is the same for both compressional and shear viscosities. It was shown by Eyring[5] that the coefficient, η, of shear viscosity is given by the expression:

$$\eta = (hN/V) \exp.(\Delta W_{vis}/\kappa T)$$

where N represents Avagadro's number and V the molar volume. Putting $\Delta W_1 = \Delta W_{vis}$ into equation 5.10a yields:

$$\tau = (\eta V/RT)\{1 + \exp.(\Delta W/\kappa T)\} \qquad (5.11a)$$

where kN equals R, the universal gas constant.

It is seen from the equation 5.10b that the height, ΔW_2, of the barrier determines the value of the relaxation time. Where this is large compared with the difference, ΔW, between the two energy levels, equation 5.10b becomes:

$$\tau = (h/\kappa T) \exp.(\Delta W_2/\kappa T) \qquad (5.11b)$$

Since $1/T$ varies at a much slower rate than exp. $(1/T)$, the relationship between τ and $1/T$ should be an exponential one. Values of τ, for water, as calculated by Hall range from 4×10^{-12} sec at $0°$ C to 0.64×10^{-12} sec at $80°$ C. These very short relaxation times account for the absence of dispersion at frequencies of the order of 10,000 Mc/s, as shown from hypersonic measurements (see Section 5.14). Respective values of relaxation times for glycerol and n-propyl alcohol, as reported by Litovitz[6], are 3.3×10^{-10} sec and 2×10^{-14} sec, respectively.

5.3. VELOCITIES IN LIQUID MIXTURES

When two unassociated liquids which do not react chemically with one another are mixed and the concentration varied, the variation of acoustic velocity with concentration is a linear one. This linear relationship does not hold when at least one of the liquids is associated.

In most cases, including that of ethyl alcohol (associated) mixed with carbon tetrachloride (unassociated), there is at first a decrease in velocity to a minimum value and then a linear increase as the concentration of alcohol is increased (see *Figure 5.3*). The probable reason for this was put forward by Derenzini and Giacomini in 1942; the molecules of ethyl alcohol, which are polar, remain as dipoles at a low concentration but as the concentration is increased the dipoles join together to form non-polar pairs. When all the molecules are grouped together in this way the velocity has reached its minimum value. As the concentration is increased still further the molecules then form non-polar groups of three or more. *Figure 5.3* shows that the value of the concentration for the minimum velocity increases with temperature.

If one of the liquids is water, the velocity-concentration curve increases to a maximum and then decreases as shown in *Figure 5.4*. The figure shows that for a concentration of 17 per cent ethyl alcohol the velocity of 1,611 m sec^{-1} remains constant for all temperatures. This is useful for the design of liquid delay lines.

5.4. PROPAGATION IN MEDIA IN THEIR CRITICAL STATES

Considerable difficulties occur when ultrasonic measurements are carried out for substances in their critical states. Nevertheless a number of results have been obtained and they indicate that maximum absorption and velocity dispersion occur in fluids at or near their critical states. This is believed to be caused by structural relaxation. When a sound wave passes through a substance in its critical state the compression phase causes liquefaction and the expansion phase gives rise to vaporization. The exchange of energy between the two states is a relaxational phenomenon.

Earlier measurements, which were conducted in substances such as carbon dioxide, ethylene and sulphur hexafluoride, because of their convenient critical temperatures, have shown the existence of relaxation peaks. There was, however, the possibility that these peaks were due to thermal relaxation. Chynoweth and Schneider[7] resolved this matter by experiments on xenon, which has a critical temperature of about 16·8° C. Xenon molecules are monatomic and thermal relaxation cannot occur for this substance. Their results for different temperatures (see *Figure 5.5*) showed low absorption except around the critical temperature at which there was a very sharp

124

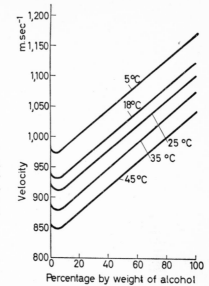

Figure 5.3. Relationship between velocity and concentration at different temperatures for a methyl alcohol–carbon tetrachloride mixture (after Derenzini and Giacomini[19])

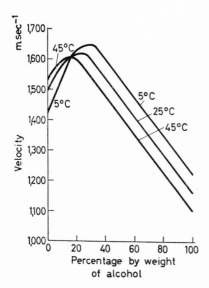

Figure 5.4. Relationship between velocity and concentration at different temperatures for an ethyl alchohol–carbon tetrachloride mixture (after Derenzini and Giacomini[19])

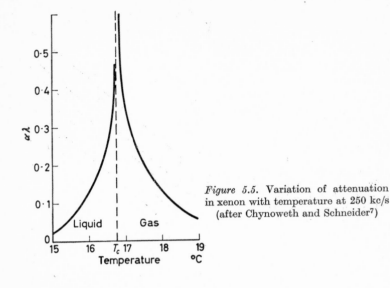

Figure 5.5. Variation of attenuation in xenon with temperature at 250 kc/s (after Chynoweth and Schneider[7])

peak. Velocity measurements at different frequencies, near the critical temperature, revealed dispersion which reached a maximum of about 6 per cent at the critical temperature. Also velocity-temperature curves showed discontinuities at this temperature (see *Figure 5.6*). The possibility that attenuation might be due to scattering caused by density inhomogeneities was considered, but it

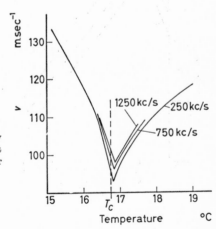

Figure 5.6. Variation of velocity with temperature at different frequencies in xenon (after Chynoweth and Schneider[7])

was shown that this could cause only a very small proportion of the enormous attenuation which was observed.

5.5. SHEAR WAVES IN LIQUIDS

5.5.1. General Considerations

Ideally a liquid should not support a shear stress but it was suggested by Poisson in 1831 that a liquid may withstand such a stress for a very limited time. This phenomenon, known as *viscoelasticity*, occurs in highly viscous liquids. Maxwell in 1867 proposed that the

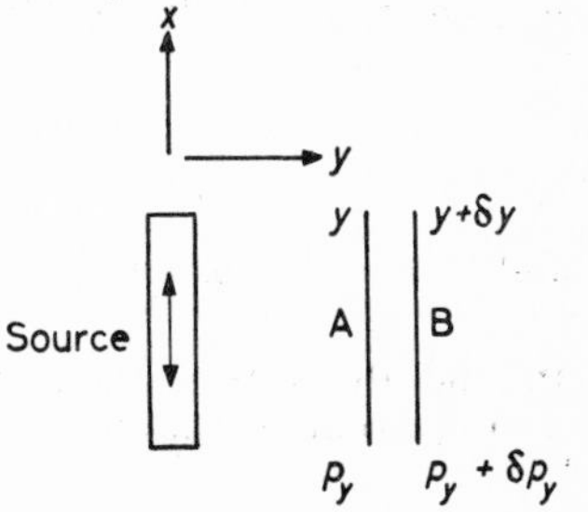

Figure 5.7. Shear wave propagation in liquids

rate of change of shear strain for a liquid subjected to a variable shear stress, p_y, is given by the equation:

$$-\frac{\partial \xi}{\partial y} = \frac{p_y}{\eta} + \frac{\dot{p}_y}{G} \tag{5.12}$$

where η and G represent the coefficients of viscosity and shear, respectively (cf. equations 4.6 and 4.7). This equation is identical in form with equation 2.40, and the solution by analogy is:

$$p_y = -\left(\frac{\partial \xi}{\partial y}\right)_0 \eta \left\{ 1 - \exp.\ \left(t \middle/ \frac{\eta}{G} \right) \right\} \tag{5.13}$$

It is seen that this is a relaxation process which is characterized by a time constant, $\tau = \eta/G$. Where p_y varies periodically, the associated relaxation frequency, f_0, is given by:

$$f_0 = 1/2\pi\tau = G/2\pi\eta \tag{5.14}$$

5.5.2. Light Liquids

For light liquids, where η may have a value of about one centipoise and where the value of G is 10^{10} dynes cm^{-2}, relaxation frequencies should be of the order of 10^5 Mc/s. Thus, except at very high frequencies, one can safely ignore the second term on the right-hand side of equation 5.12 and the expression reduces to Newton's law of viscosity, i.e. equation 5.12a, as given below. Equations expressing velocities and absorption coefficients for shear waves in liquids can be obtained by the following method for which it is assumed that the working frequency, f, is very much lower than f_0.

Consider a plane source (e.g. a Y-cut quartz crystal) vibrating along the x-direction in a liquid (see *Figure 5.7*) so that plane shear waves are propagated in the y-direction. Let A and B represent the boundaries, normal to the direction of wave propagation, of a parallel-sided layer of the liquid. The respective distances of A and B from some origin are y and $y + \delta y$. Supposing that the corresponding shear stresses at these points, at a given instant, t, be p_y and $p_y + \delta p_y$ respectively, Newton's law of viscosity gives:

$$p_y = -\eta \frac{\partial \xi}{\partial y} \text{ at A} \tag{5.12a}$$

and

$$p_y + \delta p_y = -\eta \frac{\partial \xi}{\partial y} - \frac{\partial}{\partial y}\left(\eta \frac{\partial \xi}{\partial y}\right)\delta y \text{ at B.}$$

Because these stresses must be directed in opposition to one another, we have that the resultant stress on the layer is:

$$\delta p_y = \eta \frac{\partial^2 \xi}{\partial y^2}\delta y \tag{5.15}$$

From Newton's second law of motion:

$$\delta p_y = \rho \delta y \frac{\partial \xi}{\partial t} \tag{5.16}$$

Equations 5.15 and 5.16 thus give:

$$\frac{\partial^2 \xi}{\partial y^2} = \frac{\rho}{\eta}\frac{\partial \xi}{\partial t} = 0 \tag{5.17}$$

If p_y varies as exp. $(j\omega t)$, it can be assumed that the solution is of the form:

$$\xi = A \exp.j(\omega t - k'y) \tag{5.18}$$

where A is a constant, and it is seen that $j\omega\rho = \eta k'^2$, i.e. k' is a complex quantity given by $\quad k' = (\omega\rho/2\eta)\,(1+j) \tag{5.18a}$

If one puts $k' = k + jk$, the solution may be written as:

$$\xi = A \exp. (-ky) \exp. j (\omega t - ky) \tag{5.19}$$

so that $k = a$, the absorption coefficient, which is given by:

$$a = (\omega\rho/2\eta)^{\frac{1}{2}} \tag{5.20}$$

and hence the velocity, v, is given by:

$$v = \omega/k = (2\eta\omega/\rho)^{\frac{1}{2}} \tag{5.21}$$

128

The velocity is thus frequency dependent. Attenuation is seen to decrease with viscosity and increase with frequency. Equation 5.20 shows that the motion is highly damped, even for highly viscous fluids. For example, for a liquid having a viscosity of 1,000 poises and a specific gravity of unity, this equation indicates an attenuation of 10 nepers or about 87 dB per cm at a frequency of 200 kc/s, i.e. the intensity decreases to about one-tenth of its initial value after one millimetre. For water, the attenuation per cm at this frequency is about 3,000 nepers or about 26,000 dB and intensity falls to one-tenth of its initial value after about 4×10^{-4} cm. The very short effective path lengths obtained with these waves suggest that their use should be of great value for investigating the properties of thin films of liquids such as lubricating oils.

Because of the very high attenuation of shear waves in liquids, it is not feasible to use the conventional methods of measuring their propagation constants. The properties of these waves are usually investigated by means of impedance methods (see Section 5.13) for which the two out-of-phase components of specific acoustic impedance are measured. From equation 5.19 we have:

$$\frac{\partial \xi}{\partial y} = -k(1+j)\xi$$

Combining this expression with equation 5.12a one obtains the specific acoustic impedance, Z_a, i.e.:

$$Z_a = p_y/\xi = \eta k(1+j) = \eta k(2j)^{\frac{1}{2}} \qquad (5.22)$$

Substituting $k = (\omega\rho/2\eta)^{\frac{1}{2}}$ into 5.21 we have:

$$Z_a = (\omega\rho\eta/2)^{\frac{1}{2}} (1+j) = (j\omega\rho\eta)^{\frac{1}{2}} \qquad (5.23)$$

i.e.: $\qquad Z_a = R_a + jX_a$

It is thus seen that R_a and X_a are equal in magnitude, i.e.:

$$R_a = X_a = (\omega\rho\eta/2)^{\frac{1}{2}} \qquad (5.24)$$

The acoustic path may be considered to be a transmission line (see *Figure 5.8*) consisting of a number of series impedances, Z_1, each shunted by an impedance, Z_2. Each component, Z_1, is of unit length and cross-section and the number of these components is equal to the numerical value of the acoustic path-length. Their values are given by:

$$Z_1 = j\omega\rho \text{ and } Z_2 = \eta \qquad (5.25)$$

so that: $\qquad Z_a = (Z_1 Z_2)^{\frac{1}{2}}$

129

5.5.3. *Highly Viscous Liquids*

For highly viscous fluids the second term on the right-hand side of equation 5.12 can no longer be ignored, and the relaxation frequencies given by equation 5.14 are comparatively low. For example, Mason[15] measured relaxation frequencies of about 100 kc/s in castor oil at 20° C and about 10 kc/s in polyisobutylene at 50° C. These liquids, which relax slowly, i.e. are highly viscoelastic, have been described as *non-Newtonian, Maxwellian* or *relaxing* liquids.

Where the wave frequency is high enough for the viscoelastic properties of a liquid to be prominent, a capacitance having a value $C_s = 1/G$ may be considered to shunt each element Z_2 of the transmission line described in the previous sub-section (see *Figure 5.8b*).

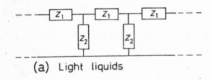

(a) Light liquids

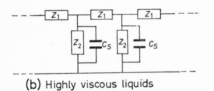

(b) Highly viscous liquids

Figure 5.8. Transmission line representation of shear wave propagation in liquids

The effective shunt impedance, Z_2', of each element is then given by the expression:

$$1/Z_2' = 1/Z_2 + j\omega C_s = 1/\eta + j\omega C_s \qquad (5.26)$$

i.e.:
$$Z_a = (Z_1 Z_2')^{\frac{1}{2}} = \left(\frac{j\omega\rho}{1/\eta + j\omega C_s} \right)^{\frac{1}{2}}$$

$$= \left(\frac{j\omega\rho\eta + \omega^2\rho\eta^2/G}{1 + \omega^2\eta^2 G^2} \right)^{\frac{1}{2}}$$

$$= \left(\frac{j\omega\rho\eta + \rho G^2\omega^2\tau^2}{1 + \omega^2\tau^2} \right)^{\frac{1}{2}} \qquad (5.27)$$

where $\tau = \eta/G$.

130

Putting $Z_a = R_a + jX_a$, we have:

$$R_a = \left\{ \frac{(\rho^2 G^2 \omega^4 \tau^4 + \omega^2 \rho^2 \eta^2)^{\frac{1}{2}} + \rho G \omega^2 \tau^2}{2(1 + \omega^2 \tau^2)} \right\}^{\frac{1}{2}} \qquad (5.28a)$$

and:

$$X_a = \left\{ \frac{(\rho^2 G^2 \omega^4 \tau^4 + \omega^2 \rho^2 \eta^2)^{\frac{1}{2}} - \rho G \omega^2 \tau^2}{2(1 + \omega^2 \tau^2)} \right\}^{\frac{1}{2}} \qquad (5.28b)$$

The phase angle is given by $\tan^{-1}(X_a/R_a)$, and by substituting $\eta = G\tau$ one obtains:

$$\frac{X_a}{R_a} = \left\{ \frac{(1 + \omega^2 \tau^2)^{\frac{1}{2}} - \omega\tau}{(1 + \omega^2 \tau^2)^{\frac{1}{2}} + \omega\tau} \right\}^{\frac{1}{2}} \qquad (5.29)$$

At low frequencies, where $\omega\tau \ll 1$, this reduces to $X_a = R_a$, i.e. the waves are purely viscous in character. At high frequencies, where $\omega\tau \gg 1$, the elements, C_s, shunt out the elements, $Z_2 = \eta$. Thus from equation 5.28 we see that X_a tends to zero, and the impedance, Z_a, is a pure resistance, R_a, such that:

$$Z_a = R_a = (\rho G)^{\frac{1}{2}} \qquad (5.20)$$

and:

$$v = Z_a / \rho = (G/\rho)^{\frac{1}{2}} \qquad (5.31)$$

Hence viscosity is no longer a consideration for wave propagation. Equation 5.31 is identical with the expression for shear waves in solids (see equation 6.1).

5.6. PROPAGATION IN LIQUID HELIUM[8, 9]

At standard pressure, helium gas liquefies at a temperature of $4 \cdot 2°$ K and it remains in the liquid state whilst it is cooled to within 10^{-6} °C of zero absolute temperature. A minimum pressure of 25 atmospheres is necessary for helium to solidify at this temperature. Liquid helium differs from all other liquids in that it exists in two phases which are separated by the λ-point, $2 \cdot 18°$ K at standard pressure. At temperatures between the boiling-point and the λ-point, the substance is called helium I and its physical properties are those typical of liquids. When helium is cooled to temperatures below the λ-point it undergoes a remarkable transformation to what is called helium II. Helium II is a thermal superconductor and also a super-fluid, i.e. its coefficient of viscosity as measured by the capillary flow method is practically zero.

The variation of the speed of sound in liquid helium with temperature is illustrated in *Figure 5.9*. The curve (a) suffers a discontinuity at the λ-point due to an abrupt change in the specific heat. The

curve representing the variation of attenuation with temperature (*Figure 5.10*) rises sharply as the temperature falls to the
λ-point. Attenuation is high in helium II at the λ-point, it decreases
to a minimum at about 2° K, and then rises steeply as the absolute
zero of temperature is approached. Curve (b) in *Figure 5.9* represents
the variation of the speed of second sound through liquid helium II.
For second sound, which can be produced by means of a thermophone (see Section 3.18), there is a periodic variation in temperature
associated with the waves, just as for ordinary sound, but there are
no changes in either pressure or density. From *Figure 5.9* it is seen

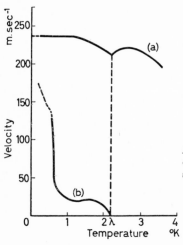

Figure 5.9. Variation of (a) the velocity
of sound and (b) the velocity of 'second
sound' with temperature in liquid
helium (after Mendelssohn[9])

that the velocity of second sound waves increases with fall in
temperature, starting from a value of zero at the λ-point, reaching
a fairly steady value of about 20 m sec^{-1} between 2° K and 1° K, and
then rising sharply in the neighbourhood of 0·7° K.

Acoustic absorption in helium I at temperatures well above the
λ-point can be fully explained by classical theory, i.e. in terms of
viscosity and thermal conductivity. The sharp increase as the λ-point
is approached is probably due to scattering caused by the appearance of small localized regions, possibly gas bubbles, in the liquid.
The high attenuation occuring in helium II at temperatures just
below the λ-point has been explained as being due to a relaxational
phenomenon connected with the equilibrium between helium I
and helium II. The increase in absorption observed in helium II at
temperatures below 1° K was predicted by Khalatnikov in 1952.
He suggested that it was a relaxation process which involved

132

interactions between energy quanta for mechanical vibrations, viz.: *phonons* and *rotons*. The phonon, which was originally introduced into the quantum theory of specific heats (see, for example, Kittel[10]) by analogy with the photon, is characteristic of translational motion. The roton, on the other hand, is concerned with rotational motion.

The existence of second sound in helium II was originally predicted by Tisza in 1939. He suggested that certain of the mechanical properties of the substance have two components, one being normal and the other connected with superfluidity. This is indicated by the

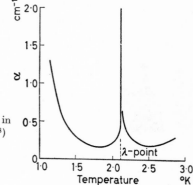

Figure 5.10. Attentuation of sound in liquid helium (after van Itterbeek[8])

fact that the viscosity of helium II as measured with a rotating viscometer has a finite value (about 3×10^{-5} poise at $1°$ K) but its value as obtained by the capillary flow method is zero. When the phase difference between these two components for the wave vectors is $180°$ there is no resultant change in either pressure or density, but the temperature variation persists. The speed, c', of second sound may be shown to be given by the relationship:

$$c' = \left(\frac{\rho_s}{\rho_n} \frac{S^2}{c_p}\right)^{\frac{1}{2}} = \left(-\frac{\rho_s}{\rho_n} \frac{dT}{d(1/S)}\right)^{\frac{1}{2}} \qquad (5.32)$$

where ρ_n and ρ_s represent, respectively, the normal and superfluid components of density, c_p the specific heat at constant pressure, T the absolute temperature, and S the entropy per unit mass.

5.7. MEASUREMENTS IN LIQUIDS

Measurements of ultrasonic velocities and absorption coefficients present fewer difficulties for liquids than for gases. The characteristic impedances of liquid media and crystal transducers do not differ from one another to any great extent, so that good acoustic coupling is easily obtained; the requirements for mounting crystal trans-ducers are thus not very stringent. Care, however, must be taken when dealing with electrically conducting liquids that there is no possibility of short-circuiting the transducer electrodes through the liquid. This may be avoided by mounting the crystal in an insulating oil which is separated from the liquid medium by a liquid-tight rubber diaphragm, as shown in *Figure 5.11*. The characteristic impedance of the type of rubber normally used for this purpose (i.e. ρc rubber) is very close to that of water.

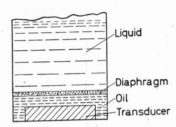

Figure 5.11. Arrangement for trans-ducer radiating into an electrically conducting liquid

In most liquids absorption is much higher than in gases and, for this reason, path lengths can be made much longer. Allowances must then be made for Fraunhofer diffraction (see Section 2.12). Because of the longer wavelengths in liquids than in gases the requirements for accuracy of parallelism between transducer and reflector surfaces are not so great; also the use of probe microphones in liquids is possible at higher frequencies.

The following methods, which have been used successfully for liquids, are discussed in the succeeding sections:

(a) Progressive wave methods.
(b) The acoustic interferometer.
(c) The pulse technique.
(d) Optical methods.
(e) The reverberation method.
(f) Impedance methods.

The final section of this chapter contains a brief discussion of the use of hypersonic waves for measurements of velocities in liquids.

5.8. PROGRESSIVE WAVE METHODS

Progressive wave methods have been used for direct measure-ments of attenuation in liquids, especially at lower frequencies. One method by Fox and Rock[12] made use of a glass bead radiometer as detector. This could be moved to any desired position in the sound field by suspending it from a carriage moving across the top of the container.

With progressive wave methods it is essential to avoid the formation of standing waves. This can be done by terminating the sound path in the liquid with highly absorbent ρc rubber or by using the technique of Biquard (see *Figure 5.12*), in which the acoustic intensity is reduced to a negligible level after successive reflections. Furthermore, precautions must be taken to eliminate what has been described as acoustical and electrical 'cross-talk' between the

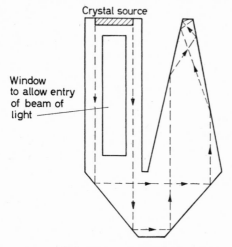

Dotted lines represent ultrasonic rays

Figure 5.12. Biquard's tank designed for eliminating stationary waves in liquids

generator and the receiver. This means that there must be no passage of sound energy between the two transducers other than through the liquid medium, and no electric currents should appear in the receiver circuit from any source other than the receiving transducer.

5.9. THE ACOUSTIC INTERFEROMETER

The use of the acoustic interferometer for liquids presents fewer problems than for gases. In addition to the points discussed in Section 5.7 it may be noted that the stringent precautions taken with gases to prevent leakage do not apply to measurements in liquids. However, one must still ensure that contamination of the liquid by any part of the interferometer is avoided.

The curves representing the variation of crystal current with reflector position are similar to those given in *Figure 4.7*, except that they are inverted, i.e. peaks and not troughs indicate that the liquid is resonating. This is due to the much higher characteristic impedances of liquids than gases, so that for resonance the amplitude of the vibrations of the crystal transducer is increased because of the higher amplitude of the vibrations in the liquid column. The consequent decrease in radiation resistance of the crystal results in an increase of current.

5.10. THE PULSE TECHNIQUE

The pulse method, in its simplest form, consists of sending a short train of sound waves through the medium to a receiver. For the transmission method the receiver is placed at a measured distance from the source, but for the echo method a reversible transducer serves as both source and receiver, a reflector being used to return the pulses. The speed of sound in the medium is then determined from the time of travel of the pulse and the acoustic path length. For a sufficiently long acoustic path, a clock will give a reasonably accurate value of this time. Langevin used this method during the 1914–18 war for measurements in sea water. A quartz sandwich transducer, which was placed on the hull of a ship, transmitted at a frequency of 40 kc/s a succession of high intensity pulses at regular intervals. These pulses, after reflection from the surface of a solid object in the water at a measured distance from the ship, were received by a similar transducer located in a suitable position on the hull of the same ship. Marks were recorded on a chart fitted to a rotating drum at the times of transmission and reception of each pulse; the speed of sound was thus calculated.

Langevin's method is not practicable for short path lengths because of the very small time intervals which would occur. For example, the time taken for sound to travel through 15 cm of water is only 10^{-4} second. It was not until after the discovery of radar that the pulse method could be used for short path lengths. It was first applied to ultrasonics for flaw detection in solids during the 1939–45 war by Sproule in Great Britain and by Firestone in the U.S.A., and for measurements in liquids by Pelham and Galt in 1946.

The use of the pulse technique for solids is described in some detail in Section 6.11 and similar principles apply to measurements in liquids. For liquids, however, one can vary the acoustic path length by means of a movable reflector. Measurements of attenuation are thus possible from the observation of the height of a single deflection on the screen of the cathode ray oscilloscope whilst the reflector is moved. Here again, precautions must be taken to ensure parallelism between the source and the reflector, or receiver, and allowance must be made for diffraction and wave-guide effects.

One advantage of this method is that energy passes through the medium for only a small fraction of the time during which measurements are made. Thus it is possible to propagate waves having high energy densities without any appreciable heating of the medium.

5.11. OPTICAL METHODS

5.11.1. General Considerations

Optical techniques for measuring ultrasonic propagation constants include the striation and optical diffraction methods. They depend on the variations of refractive indices brought about by periodic

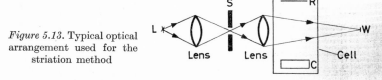

Figure 5.13. Typical optical arrangement used for the striation method

changes in density due to sound waves passing through transparent media. One advantage of using optical techniques is that velocity measurements can be made on small samples of materials. Furthermore, when the optical system is set up once for all, measurements on different samples can be made in rapid succession. For reasons which will appear self-evident, these methods are restricted to frequencies in the megacycle range.

5.11.2. The Striation Method

Toepler in 1866 (Bergman[13], p. 58) developed the striation method for rendering sound waves visible and thus enabling the measurement of wavelengths. The sharp image of a vertical slit, S (see *Figure 5.13*) which is illuminated by a source of monochromatic light, L, is focussed on to a vertical wire, W. This causes the light beam to be completely interrupted when no sound is radiated. Stationary waves set up in the vessel by the crystal, C, and reflector, R, give rise to periodic refractions of the light beam, and the beam of light is displaced so as to pass the wire, W. A series of equidistant light and dark parallel fringes are observed with a telescope focussed on W. The distance of separation of these fringes is directly proportional to the wavelength so that at higher frequencies the fringes move closer together. At lower frequencies, because of more gradual changes of refractive indices, the fringe visibility decreases, thereby setting a lower frequency limit to the use of this device. Bergman[13] (p. 62), using a stroboscopic technique, applied the striation method to progressive waves.

5.11.3. The Optical Diffraction Method

The optical diffraction method resulted from the discoveries made in 1932 by Debye and Sears, and Lucas and Biquard, independently of one another, that a parallel beam of ultrasonic waves in a transparent medium acts as a diffraction grating for light. For a stationary wave system, the periodic variation of refractive index produces a grating with a spacing of $\lambda/2$, where λ represents the acoustic wavelength. For a progressive wave system, the grating has a spacing of λ and it moves with the speed of sound. However, the speed of sound is negligible compared with that of light and the grating is effectively stationary.

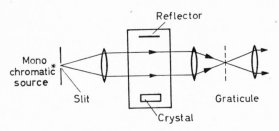

Figure 5.14. Typical optical arrangement for use with the optical diffraction method for stationary waves

When a parallel beam of monochromatic light waves of wavelength Λ, is incident at right-angles to an acoustic grating, the angle, θ, of diffraction is given by:

$$\sin \theta = 2n\Lambda/\lambda \qquad \text{for stationary waves} \qquad (5.33\text{a})$$

or:

$$\sin \theta = n\Lambda/\lambda \qquad \text{for progressive waves} \qquad (5.33\text{b})$$

where n is an integer, which can be positive or negative depending on whether θ is positive or negative.

The optical arrangement for this method is given in *Figure 5.14.* A collimator produces a parallel beam of light from a monochromatic slit source. The beams are brought, after diffraction, to a focus at the focal plane of the telescope objective. In general, a number of parallel images of the slit having different intensities is observed (see *Figure 5.15*). These images arise from the diffraction of the

Figure 5.15. Diffracted images of a sodium slit source obtained with the optical diffraction method

Figure 5.16. Optical diffraction apparatus used by the author

To face p. 138.

beam of light by angles having different values of θ; they are referred to as spectral lines of the nth order, the value of n being given by equations 5.33. For a source of light of given wavelength, the distance of separation of a given order spectral line from the zeroth order line depends on the value of θ, which increases with decreasing wavelength, i.e. increasing frequency. To achieve a reasonable degree of accuracy in measuring this distance one must use frequencies in the megacycle range.

The distribution of optical intensities among the various spectral lines differs here from that observed with an ordinary two-dimensional ruled grating, because the acoustically formed grating is a three-dimensional one. For the two-dimensional grating the maximum intensity occurs in the zeroth order image of the slit and the intensity decreases as the spectral order increases. For the acoustic grating the optical intensity of the spectral lines is such a function of the acoustic intensity that as the latter is increased more light is diverted away from the zeroth order spectrum into the higher order spectra. The decrease in proportional intensity of the zeroth order line has been shown to be proportional to the intensity of the sound wave.

The diffraction method may thus be used for measuring both velocities and absorption coefficients. Absorption coefficients are determined by measuring the optical intensity of the zeroth order spectrum with a photoelectric cell as the beam of light is moved across the sound field. Attenuation measurements using this method are best carried out with progressive waves and, provided that the absorption is not too high, a degree of accuracy comparable with that obtainable with the pulse method is possible.

This technique has been used by the author for comparing velocities in various liquids and liquid mixtures (see *Figure 5.16*). The crystal source, an X-cut quartz plate resonating at a frequency of 10 Mc/s, was mounted in oil so as to radiate upwards into a steel plate (see *Figure 5.17*). The liquid medium was contained in a rectangular glass cell placed on the steel plate, acoustic coupling being effected by means of a thin film of glycerine, and the whole apparatus was mounted on the table of an optical spectrometer. Because its upper surface acted as a reflector, stationary waves were formed in the liquid. The distance of separation of the spectral lines was measured by a graticule in the eyepiece of the spectrometer telescope. The graticule reading was proportional to sin θ, to a sufficiently high degree of accuracy, and thus inversely proportional to wavelength and, hence, velocity. The instrument was calibrated using water, in which the velocity was known.

Because the glass cell could be easily removed and replaced, this method provided a convenient and rapid method of measuring acoustic velocities. It was found, in practice, that the magnitude of the standing wave ratio in the liquid made no appreciable difference

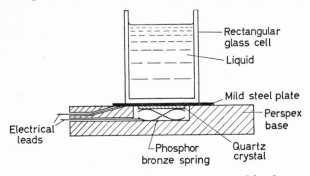

Figure 5.17. Diagram of the arrangement used by the author for diffraction measurements

to the visibility of the spectral lines, so that it was not necessary to adjust the height of the liquid. It was verified, by means of a wavemeter, that no variation in frequency occurred when changing the liquid.

5.12. THE REVERBERATION METHOD

The reverberation method, which is commonly used in architectural acoustics, has been applied to the measurements of absorption coefficients in liquids and it has proved successful at frequencies

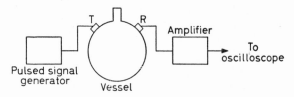

Figure 5.18. Reverberation method (after Karpovich[3])

in the upper kilocycle range. The liquid may be contained in a spherical or cylindrical vessel which is supported so as to suffer a minimum of damping. This is best achieved by suspending the vessel in vacuo by means of fine wires.

With the method of Karpovich[3] (see *Figure 5.18*) a crystal generator, T, is cemented to one part of the vessel's surface and a receiver, R, to another part of it. Radiation from the transmitting crystal is reflected successively from the walls of the vessel so that there is a diffuse sound field in the liquid. In a very short time a steady state is reached for which the energy density throughout the medium is constant and the pressure amplitude, p, at the receiver is steady and equal to p_0. On switching off the source, p decreases exponentially with time, t, such that

$$p = p_0 \exp.(- a't) \tag{5.34}$$

where a' is defined by equation 2.5. The transmitter is excited at regular intervals by means of square-shaped pulses and the output of the receiver is amplified logarithmically and fed to the Y-plates of a cathode ray oscilloscope, the time base of which is synchronized with the pulse trigger. A straight line having a negative slope, a', thus appears on the screen of the oscilloscope. A correction is necessary for absorption by the material of the container.

At low frequencies the output of the receiver may be fed into a high-speed level recorder. In this case the source need only be excited by a single pulse.

5.13. IMPEDANCE METHODS

The methods which have been described in the preceding sections, are unsuitable where the absorption is too high for any appreciable degree of penetration of the medium by the sound waves to occur, e.g. the transmission of shear waves through liquids. Impedance methods, however, can be used in these circumstances because only the effects of the reaction of the medium on the source, or on another medium directly in contact with the source, are measured. For such a method one must know the relationships between the real and imaginary components of specific acoustic impedance, and the propagation constants. For shear waves in liquids these relationships have been derived in Section 5.5; for compressional waves they are obtained as follows:

Particle displacement, ξ, may be expressed in the form:

$$\xi = A \exp.(- ax) \exp. j(\omega t - kx) \tag{5.35}$$

for plane progressive waves (see equation 2.38c). It is assumed that attenuation is sufficiently high for the formation of stationary waves to be avoided. We thus have:

$$\dot{\xi} = j\omega\xi$$

and:
$$p = - \rho c^2\left(\frac{\partial \xi}{\partial x}\right) = (a + jk)\rho c^2 \xi$$

(see equation 2.27a). Specific acoustic impedance, Z_a, is thus given by:

$$Z_a = p/\dot{\xi} = \rho c^2 (a + jk)/j\omega = \rho c (1 - j\,a/k) \qquad (5.36)$$

i.e.:
$$Z_a = R_a + jX_a \qquad (5.36a)$$

where R_a and X_a are respectively the resistive and reactive components of the complex impedance. Their values are given by:

$$R_a = \rho c \text{ and } X_a = -\,a/k \qquad (5.37)$$

A method devised by Paetzold, Guettner, and Bastir (see Hueter and Bolt[14], p. 354) comprises the measurement of the frequency response of the transducer when it is loaded by the medium. A

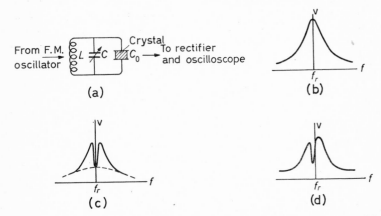

(a)

(b)

(c)

(d)

Figure 5.19. Method of Paetzold *et al.* for impedance measurements: (*a*) arrangement of crystal and tuned circuit; (*b*) response curve for clamped crystal; (*c*) response curve for oscillating crystal (low attenuation) (dotted line represents response when parallel C_0 and R substituted for the crystal) (*d*) response curve for oscillating crystal (high attenuation)

crystal transducer having a natural frequency, f_r, is connected in parallel with a tuned LC circuit (see *Figure 5.19a*). The value of the inductance, L, and the capacitance, C, are chosen so that when the crystal is clamped:

$$f_r = 1/2\pi\{L(C + C_0)\}^{\frac{1}{2}} \qquad (5.38)$$

where C_0 is the clamped electrical capacitance of the crystal. A constant current frequency modulated signal which 'warbles' over a frequency range of ± 10 per cent about f_r is applied to the system, and the resultant voltage is rectified and then fed to the Y-plates of a cathode ray oscilloscope, the time base of which is synchronized with the modulation frequency. When the transducer is clamped, the response curve shown in *Figure 5.19b* is observed on the screen of the oscilloscope. When the transducer is allowed to oscillate, the effect of the equivalent tuned circuit of the crystal (see Section 3.4.2), which is in parallel with the LC circuit, is to reduce the peak of the response curve to a crevasse (see *Figure 5.19c*). The depth of the crevasse, which is determined initially by the friction of the crystal mounting, decreases with increase in loading. Where attenuation in the medium is low, the loading is almost entirely resistive and the crevasse is symmetrical with respect to the response curve. The effect of any appreciable attenuation is to introduce a reactive component to the impedance of the loading medium and the crevasse is no longer symmetrical in relation to the curve (see *Figure 5.19d*).

Where the mounting resistance of the transducer is negligible, or where it can be allowed for, the measurements of resistance may be made as follows. The crystal is first allowed to oscillate in a medium such as water, having a known impedance, $\rho_0 c_0$, and the depth of the crevasse noted. The transducer is then disconnected from the circuit and replaced by a capacitance having the same value, C_0, as that for the clamped transducer. A resistance box which is shunted across the electrodes is adjusted to a value, R_0, so that the peak of the response curve, as indicated by the dotted line in *Figure 5.19c*, coincides with the position of the bottom of the crevasse. This is the equivalent electrical resistance of the load as given by $R_0 = R_m/a_T{}^2 = \rho_0 c_0 A/a_T{}^2$ (see equation 3.27), where a_T represents the transformation factor for the transducer. This procedure is then repeated for the test medium, which has an impedance, ρc, for which the equivalent electrical resistance is R. Hence we have:

$$R/R_0 = \rho c/\rho_0 c_0 \qquad (5.39)$$

The reactive component of the impedance is obtained by varying C by an amount ΔC until the crevasse is symmetrical about the response peak. The equivalent circuit of the loading medium is then a resistance, R, in parallel with a capacitance, ΔC. This is equivalent to a resistance $R/\{1 + \omega_0{}^2 R^2 (\Delta C)^2\}$ in series with a reactance $\omega_0{}^2 R^2 \Delta C/\{1 + \omega_0{}^2 R^2 (\Delta C)^2\}$

Thus:
$$\frac{\omega_0 R^2 \Delta C}{R} = \frac{X_a}{R_a} = \frac{a}{\rho c k}$$

i.e.:
$$a = \omega_0 \rho c k R \Delta C \qquad (5.40)$$

Mason[15] (p. 339) has described shear wave measurements in viscous liquids with the transducer performing torsional oscillations.

In one example an ADP crystal was cut in the form of a hollow cylinder with the geometric axis coinciding with the crystallographic X-axis. The whole of the interior surface of the crystal was plated to form an electrode and the outer surface was plated on two opposite 90° quadrants in such a way that the plane bisecting these quadrants coincided with the Z-axis. These quadrants were connected electrically. The transducer was supported at nodal points by means of three wires, which also provided electrical contact with the electrodes. Contact with the inner electrode was effected by means of a narrow strip of plating extending from the wire support along the outer surface, between the two quadrants, and over the edge to join the inner plated surface. Torsional vibrations could then be excited by the application of an alternating voltage

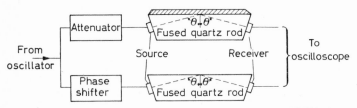

Figure 5.20. Shear wave reflection method of Mason and McSkimin

between the inner and outer surfaces of the crystal. For light liquids the impedance of the load could be determined by measuring the resistance, R_0, of the transducer and its frequency, f_r, at resonance, firstly *in vacuo* and then in the medium. Mason showed that the components, R_a and X_a, of the impedance of the medium were directly proportional to the differences, ΔR_0 and Δf_r, the constants of proportionality depending only upon the physical properties of the transducer. For very viscous fluids the exact position of resonance could not be accurately located and a bridge circuit was used for determining the resistive and reactive components. This method has been used with frequencies of up to about 200 kc/s.

For measurements in the megacycle range, Mason and McSkimin in 1952 (see Hueter and Bolt[14], p. 366), used a shear wave reflection technique. Their apparatus consisted of two identical fused quartz rods (see *Figure 5.20*) with the ends inclined at an angle, θ, to the horizontal. Similar Y-cut or AT-cut quartz crystals were mounted on the ends and orientated so that shear waves which were polarized in the direction parallel with the top surface were propagated; they were internally reflected as shown. The value of the angle of incidence to the top surface was such that no longitudinal waves were produced by mode conversion (see Section 2.11.3). The output signals

144

from the receivers were compared with one another by means of a cathode ray oscilloscope and balance was obtained initially with no load on either quartz rod. By placing the liquid under test on the top surface of one of the rods the balance was upset. This was restored by suitable adjustment of the attenuator and phase shifter. If r represents the ratio of amplitudes of the attenuated and unattenuated signals and ϕ represents the phase shift, then it can be shown that the load impedance, Z_a, of the liquid is given by:

$$Z_a = Z' \cos \theta \, (1 - r^2 + 2jr \sin \phi)/(1 + r^2 + 2r \cos \phi) \qquad (5.41)$$

where Z' represents the shear wave impedance of the fused quartz.

5.14. HYPERSONIC WAVES IN LIQUIDS[16–18]

Much work has been done, especially in India, on the propagation through liquids of ultrasonic waves of thermal origin, i.e. thermal phonons, having frequencies exceeding 1,000 Mc/s. These waves are called *hypersonic* or *ultra high frequency* (UHF) waves and are caused by the thermal activation of the lattice structure of the liquid. Because the vibrations are of a random nature, their frequencies are distributed continuously in bands.

Brillouin, in 1922, predicted that if a monochromatic beam of light passes through a liquid through which sound is propagated, scattering of the beam may occur in the same way as a beam of X-rays is scattered by a crystal lattice. The scattered light should be visible at a glancing angle, θ, in accordance with Bragg's relation, i.e.:

$$\varLambda = 2 \lambda \sin \theta \qquad (5.42)$$

Here λ and $\varLambda$ represent the acoustic and optical wavelengths, respectively. This equation holds in practice only when the two wavelengths are of a similar order of magnitude, i.e. for frequencies in the hypersonic range.

Because the sound waves are moving with a velocity, c, a Doppler effect is produced and there is an apparent change in optical wavelength given by:

$$\pm \delta \varLambda = (2 \varLambda c \cos \theta)/C \qquad (5.43)$$

where C represents the speed of light.

The sign appended to $\varDelta \lambda$ indicates the relative directions of $c \cos \theta$ and C. Thus, by measuring the change in wavelength of a source of monochromatic light, the speed of sound in the liquid can be calculated. This method has been used for measuring the velocity dispersion of thermally activated phonons. Using a

Fabry Perot interferometer an accuracy of about 10 per cent is possible.

REFERENCES

1. ROBERTS, J. K. and MILLER, A. R. *Heat and Thermodynamics*, 5th Edn., Blackie, London
2. ANDREA, J. H., HEASALL, E. and LAMB, J. *Proc. Phys. Soc.*, 1956, **B69**, 625
3. KARPOVICH, J. *J. chem. Phys.*, 1954, **22**, 1767
4. HALL, L. *Phys. Rev.*, 1948, **73**, 775
5. EYRING, H. *J. chem. Phys.*, 1936, **4**, 283
6. LITOVITZ, T. A. *J. acoust. Soc. Amer.*, 1959, **31**, 681
7. CHYNOWETH, A. G. and SCHNEIDER, W. G. *J. chem. Phys.*, 1952, **30**, 1777
8. VAN ITTERBEEK, A. *Progress in Low Temperature Physics* (ed. C. J. Gorter), Vol. 1, N. Holland Publ. Co., Amsterdam, 1955
9. MENDELSSOHN, K. *Cryophysics*, Interscience, New York, 1960
10. KITTEL, C. *An Introduction to Solid State Physics*, 2nd Edn., Wiley, NewYork/Chapman and Hall, London, 1956
11. LINDSAY, R. B. *Mechanical Radiation*, McGraw-Hill, New York, 1960
12. FOX, G. F. and ROCK, G. D. *J. acoust. Soc. Amer.*, 1941, **12**, 505
13. BERGMANN, L. *Ultrasonics* (trans. H. S. Hatfield) Wiley, NewYork/ Bell, London, 1938
14. HUETER, T. F. and BOLT, R. H. *Sonics*, Wiley, New York/Chapman and Hall, London, 1955
15. MASON, W. P. *Piezoelectric Crystals and their Application to Ultrasonics*, van Nostrand, New York, 1950
16. KITTEL, C. *Rep. Prog. Phys.*, 1948, **11**, 232
17. RICHARDSON, E. G. *Ultrasonic Physics*, 2 Edn., Elsevier, Amsterdam, 1962
18. HERZFELD, K. F. and LITOVITZ, T. A. *Absorption and Dispersion of Ultrasonics*, Academic Press, New York, 1959
19. DERENZINI, T. and GIACOMINI, A. *Ric. Sci.*, 1942, **13**, 27 and 242
20. KAYE, G. W. C. and LABY, T. H. *Tables of Physical and Chemical Constants*, 11th Edn., Longmans, Green, London, 1957

6

LOW AMPLITUDE PROPAGATION IN SOLIDS

6.1. VELOCITIES IN SOLIDS

THE mechanical properties of solids differ from those of fluids in two important respects. Firstly, greater binding forces exist between their constituent atoms so that they will, in general, support shear stresses. Secondly, anisotropy may occur, especially in single crystals, in which the atoms form regular lattices. The stress-strain relationships for anisotropic solids vary with direction and are expressed in the form of equation 3.11.

An isotropic solid may be either amorphous, for which the lattice structure is a random one similar to that of a liquid, or polycrystalline, for which there are a large number of crystalline grains or crystallites orientated at random. The elastic properties of an isotropic solid do not vary with direction.

Consider a thin layer of a solid (see *Figure 2.3*) and let a compressive stress in the x-direction be applied to the layer. It can be shown (see, for example, Champion and Davy[1], p. 86) that this stress is equivalent to a uniform compression and a shear stress acting simultaneously. One would thus expect that the corresponding elastic modulus would be a function of the bulk modulus, K, and the rigidity, G; it is, in fact, $K + 4G/3$.

The velocity, c_L, of plane longitudinal waves is thus given in accordance with equation 2.26, by the expression:

$$c_L = \left\{ \left(K_S + \frac{4}{3}G_S \right) / \rho \right\}^{\frac{1}{2}} \tag{6.1}$$

where the suffix, S, indicates adiabatic changes. From the relationships which exist between the various elastic constants (see, for example, Champion and Davy[1], p. 52) equation 6.1 may be written alternatively as:

$$c_L = \left\{ \frac{Y_S(1 - \sigma_S)}{\rho(1 + \sigma_S)(1 - 2\sigma_S)} \right\}^{\frac{1}{2}} \tag{6.1a}$$

where Y represents the Young's modulus and σ the Poisson's ratio for the medium.

Where a pure shear stress acts on the layer it suffers only a shear strain and the appropriate elastic modulus is the rigidity, G.

147

The velocity, c_T, of plane shear waves in the solid is thus given by the expression:

$$c_T = (G_S/\rho)^{\frac{1}{2}} \qquad (6.2)$$

Values of elastic constants and acoustic velocities for various polycrystalline materials are listed in *Table 6.1*, from which it can be seen that the shear wave velocity for a given substance is about half the compression wave velocity.

Table 6.1. Values of Elastic Moduli and Acoustic Velocities for some Metals in Polycrystalline Form
The velocities were calculated from values of elastic constants given by Kaye and Laby[51]

Metal	Young's Modulus Y newtons m^{-2} $\times 10^{-10}$	Bulk Modulus K newtons m^{-2} $\times 10^{-10}$	Rigidity G newtons m^{-2} $\times 10^{-10}$	Density ρ g cm^{-3}	Velocity of Longitudinal Waves — Solids in bulk m sec^{-1}	Velocity of Longitudinal Waves — Rods m sec^{-1}	Velocity of shear waves m sec^{-1}
Aluminium (worked)	7·05	7·46	2·63	2·7	6,400	5,100	3,100
Copper	12·3	13·1	4·55	8·9	4,700	3,700	1,200
Gold	8·0	16·6	2·80	19·3	3,200	2,000	1,200
Iron	21·3	16·1	8·31	7·9	5,900	5,200	3,200
Lead	1·62	5·0	0·56	11·3	2,300	1,200	790
Nickel	20·2	17·6	7·7	8·9	5,600	4,800	2,900
Platinum	16·8	24·7	6·04	21·45	3,900	2,800	1,700
Silver	7·9	10·9	2·86	10·5	3,700	2,700	1,600
Steel (worked)	20·9	16·4	8·12	7·8	6,000	5,200	2,900
Tin	5·43	5·29	2·04	7·3	3,300	2,700	1,700

For a solid in the form of a rod, where the cross-sectional dimensions are small compared with wavelength, the velocity, c_w, of longitudinal waves in the axial direction is given by the equation:

$$c_w = (Y/\rho)^{\frac{1}{2}} \qquad (6.3)$$

A number of ultrasonic applications involve the propagation of waves across the surfaces of solids. It has been shown (see, for example, Champion and Davy[1], p. 91) that there are two types of these *surface waves*. The first, polarized in the plane of the surface and at right-angles to the direction of motion, is called *Love waves* and the other *Rayleigh waves*. For Rayleigh waves the wave vector has two components, one longitudinal and the other transverse, at right-angles to the surface. Surface waves do not penetrate appreciably into the interior of a solid and propagation thus takes place in only two dimensions. The attenuation of these waves is consequently very much less than that of waves which do penetrate into the solid. The velocity, c_R, of Rayleigh waves may be shown (see, for example, Redwood[2], p. 50) to be expressed as follows:

$$\left(\frac{c_R}{c_T}\right)^2 \left\{\frac{c_R{}^6}{c_T{}^6} - \frac{8c_R{}^4}{c_T{}^4} + c_R{}^2\left(\frac{24}{c_T{}^2} - \frac{16}{c_L{}^2}\right) - 16\left(1 - \frac{c_T{}^2}{c_L{}^2}\right)\right\} = 0 \quad (6.4)$$

Here c_T and c_L represent, respectively, the shear and longitudinal wave velocities for the material. The Rayleigh wave velocity is the particular solution for c_R for which its value is slightly less than that of c_T. For example, where Poisson's ratio has a value of $\frac{1}{4}$, $c_R = 0.92\, c_T$ is the required solution.

Plane wave velocities in single crystals are dependent upon the directions of propagation. Expressions for these velocities contain the components, c_{hk}, of the elastic constants given by equation 3.11; the forms of these expressions are dependent upon the crystalline structure of the solid (see Mason[3], p. 368). For a cubic crystal the velocities along the different axes are expressed in *Table 6.2*, in which values for germanium are given.

An important application of velocity measurements for both longitudinal and shear waves is the determination of the elastic constants along the various axes of single crystals over very wide ranges of temperature. The determination of the anisotropy of acoustic velocities and, hence, elastic constants can yield useful information about other physical properties of the crystal. For example, in metals and certain semi-conductors[4], thermal conduction arises from the motion of free electrons and from the lattice vibrations, i.e. phonons. The degree of anisotropy of the ultrasonic velocities in a single crystal of such a material should agree with that for the lattice vibration components of thermal conductivity.

6.2. ULTRASONIC ATTENUATION IN SOLIDS

The absorption of ultrasonic waves in solids may be attributed to a number of different causes, each of which is characteristic of the physical properties of the medium concerned, although the exact nature of the cause of attenuation may not always be properly understood. However, an attempt is made here to classify the various known and possible causes of attenuation and to discuss them under the following headings:

(a) Losses characteristic of polycrystalline solids.

(b) Absorption due to lattice imperfections.

(c) Absorption in ferromagnetic and ferroelectric materials.

(d) Absorption due to electron-phonon interactions.

(e) Absorption in single crystals due to thermal effects.

(f) Absorption due to other possible causes.

In Section 6.9 a brief account is given of the effect of illumination on acoustic attenuation in a photoconducting medium.

Table 6.2. Acoustic Velocities along the Axes of Cubic Crystals, with Values for Germanium at Room Temperature obtained by McSkimin[50]

Direction of propagation	Direction of polarization	Type of wave	Velocity	Velocity in germanium m sec⁻¹
100	100	Longitudinal	$(c_{11}/\rho)^{\frac{1}{2}}$	4,920
	010	Shear	$(c_{44}/\rho)^{\frac{1}{2}}$	—
	001	Shear	$(c_{44}/\rho)^{\frac{1}{2}}$	3,540
110	110	Longitudinal	$\{(c_{11}+c_{12}+2c_{44})/2\rho\}^{\frac{1}{2}}$	5,400
	001	Shear	$(c_{44}/\rho)^{\frac{1}{2}}$	3,550
	$1\bar{1}0$	Shear	$\{(c_{11}-c_{12})/2\rho\}^{\frac{1}{2}}$	2,750
111	111	Longitudinal	$\{(c_{11}+2c_{12}+4c_{44})/3\rho\}^{\frac{1}{2}}$	—
	Any direction in 111 plane	Shear	$\{(c_{11}-c_{12}+c_{44})/3\rho\}^{\frac{1}{2}}$	—

Density of germanium $= 5\cdot46$ g cm⁻³

From the values of velocity given above the following results are obtained for germanium

$$c_{11} = 13\cdot2 \times 10^{10} \text{ newton m}^{-2}$$
$$c_{12} = 4\cdot9 \times 10^{10} \text{ newton m}^{-2}$$
$$c_{44} = 6\cdot8 \times 10^{10} \text{ newton m}^{-2}$$

6.3. LOSSES CHARACTERISTIC OF POLYCRYSTALLINE SOLIDS

6.3.1. Thermoelastic Relaxation

A polycrystalline solid may be isotropic because of the random orientation of the constituent grains although the individual grains may themselves be anisotropic. Thus, when a given stress is applied to this kind of solid there will be a variation of strain from one grain to another. A compression causes a rise in temperature in each crystallite but, because of the inhomogeneity of the resultant strain, the temperature distribution is not a uniform one. Thus, during the compression half of an acoustic cycle, heat will flow from a grain that has suffered the greater strain, and is consequently at a higher

150

temperature, to one which has suffered a lesser strain and, as a result, is at a lower temperature. A reversal in the direction of the heat flow takes place during the expansion half of a cycle.

This is clearly a relaxation process which gives rise to absorption (see Section 2.10.2). Zener[5] showed that the absorption coefficient, α, for this effect is given by the expression:

$$\alpha = \frac{C_p - C_v}{C_v} \frac{(R)}{2c} \frac{\omega_0 \omega^2}{\omega_0^2 + \omega^2} \tag{6.5}$$

where $f_0 = \omega_0/2\pi$, the relaxation frequency, is given by:

$$f_0 \simeq K/\rho C_p L_c^2$$

Here c is the acoustic velocity, C_p and C_v represent the molar heats at constant pressure and volume, respectively, K the coefficient of thermal conductivity, and L_c the average grain diameter. (R) is a function which depends upon the average fluctuation of strain energy due to anisotropy; some values of (R) calculated by Zener are given in *Table 6.3*. For most materials f_0 is less than 100 kc/s.

Table 6.3. Effect of Elastic Anisotropy in Cubic Crystals (see equation 6.5)
Values calculated by Zener[5]

Substance	(R)	$(C_p - C_v)/C_v$	*Product*
Lead	0·065	0·067	$4·4 \times 10^{-3}$
Silver	0·031	0·040	$1·2 \times 10^{-3}$
Copper	0·031	0·028	$8·7 \times 10^{-4}$
Gold	0·014	0·038	$5·3 \times 10^{-4}$
Iron	0·022	0·016	$3·5 \times 10^{-4}$
Aluminium	0·0009	0·046	4×10^{-5}
Tungsten	10^{-6}	0·006	6×10^{-9}

Because a change in volume is required for these losses to occur, attenuation caused by thermoelastic relaxation cannot take place for shear waves.

6.3.2. *Grain Boundary Losses*

Grain boundary losses also occur as a result of the random orientation of the anisotropic grains in a polycrystalline solid. Consider an acoustic beam travelling through this type of solid in a given direction. At each grain boundary there is a discontinuity of elastic modulus and, hence, in the characteristic impedance for the

beam. Reflections thus take place at the boundaries and the resultant loss depends on the degree of anisotropy of the crystallites, the
mean grain diameter, L_c, and wavelength, λ.

Where the wavelength is small compared with the grain size, the
losses are caused by regular reflections. Mason and McSkimin[6]
showed that the resultant attenuation should vary inversely with
the mean grain diameter but remain independent of frequency. On
the other hand where the wavelength is large compared with grain
size, Rayleigh-type scattering should occur and the attenuation is
proportional to the fourth power of the frequency and to the cube
of the mean grain diameter, i.e.:

$$a = L_c{}^3(S)/\lambda^4 = L_c{}^3(S)f^4/c^4 \qquad (6.6)$$

(S) represents the anisotropy factor for which typical values are
given in Table 6.4.

Table 6.4. Values of the 'Anisotropy' Factor (S) for Various Metals (see
equation 6.6)
Based on calculated values given by Mason[3], p. 208

Metal	(S) Longitudinal waves	(S) Shear waves
Aluminium	0·026	0·29
Gold	0·16	4·5
Silver	0·43	5·3
Copper	0·64	5·8
Lead	0·36	6·2
Iron	0·58	3·5
Sodium	2·5	11
Potassium	1·5	9·5
Tungsten	0	0
Magnesium	0·19	—
Zinc	4·9	—
Cadmium	2·4	—

Mason and McSkimin have predicted an additional loss due to
elastic hysteresis at the grain boundaries. This loss is proportional
to the first power of the frequency but independent of the grain
size or type of wave. Where it occurs with Rayleigh-type scattering
the total absorption is given by the expression:

$$a = B_1 f + B_2 f^4$$

where B_1 and B_2 are constants for a given material and type of wave. Rayleigh scattering is not significant at frequencies below 1 Mc/s.

Huntingdon[7] considered attenuation for conditions lying between $\lambda \gg L_c$ and $\lambda \ll L_c$. By assuming that diffraction is caused by the small volume elements having different characteristic impedances, he showed that the attenuation is directly proportional to the square of the product of the mean grain diameter and the frequency.

6.4. ABSORPTION DUE TO LATTICE IMPERFECTIONS

6.4.1. General Considerations

Any departure from regularity in the lattice structure for a crystalline solid is regarded as an imperfection, which may give rise to acoustic absorption. Imperfections include point defects, such as lattice vacancies and the presence of impurity atoms, and dislocations, i.e. line defects.

6.4.2. Impurity Atoms

With the introduction of an impurity (the solute) into a solid (the solvent), the atoms of the impurity can be described as either interstitial or substitutional. Interstitial atoms are those which occupy positions between the atoms forming the lattice and substitutional atoms are those which displace some of the lattice atoms from their regular positions. Interstitial atoms arise where the solute and solvent atoms differ considerably in size, whereas substitutional atoms occur where the solute and solvent atoms are about the same size, usually to within 15 per cent.

The mechanism for absorption due to the presence of impurities is best explained for carbon or nitrogen impurities in iron, where the C or N atoms lie interstitially within the Fe lattice. Iron crystals have a body-centred cubic structure and the interstitial positions are the face centres and the mid-points of the edges (see *Figure 6.1*). For an unstrained body the energy levels are the same for all of these interstitial positions. Consider a compression applied along the X-direction, caused by the passage of sound waves. The Fe atoms are brought closer together along the X-direction and moved further apart along the Y- and Z-directions. The energy levels for positions such as A are thus raised and those for positions such as B and C are lowered so that an impurity atom at A moves to either B or C. During the expansion half of the acoustic cycle an atom at B or C moves to a position, A. The finite time required for this exchange of energy is responsible for relaxation and, hence, acoustic absorption.

This effect has been observed also for carbon, nitrogen, and oxygen impurities in tantalum and tungsten and for zinc atoms in copper. At room temperatures the relaxation times may be too long for ultrasonic absorption to be observed and it would be necessary to raise the temperature to obtain shorter times. The variation of

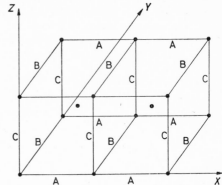

Figure 6.1. Positions of inter-stitial atoms in a Fe lattice

relaxation time, τ, with temperature is similar to that expressed by equation 5.11b and is given by the relationship:

$$\tau = \tau_0 \exp. \ (W/\kappa T) \qquad (6.7)$$

where κ is Boltzmann's constant, T the temperature in degrees K and W the activation energy. For carbon in steel we have $\tau_0 = 4 \cdot 5 \times 10^{-14}$ sec and $W = 0 \cdot 78$ eV. Putting $\kappa = 8 \cdot 6 \times 10^{-5}$ eV deg. C^{-1} it is seen that at room temperature τ is approximately $0 \cdot 5$ sec and a relaxation frequency of 1 Mc/s occurs for a temperature of about 150° C.

6.4.3. Dislocations

Dislocations in a crystal can take a number of forms and the

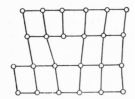

Figure 6.2. Edge type dislocation in a cubic crystal

reader is referred to Cottrell[8] for a detailed account of their proper-ties and Kittel[9] for a more elementary discussion. The simplest kind of dislocation is the edge type which is illustrated in *Figure 6.2*.

Dislocations can be introduced into a crystal by applying a stress sufficiently high to exceed the elastic limit, e.g. by the process of cold working or even by ill-treatment. When smaller subsequent stresses are applied the dislocations may travel through the crystal (see *Figure 6.3*). A network of dislocations will be formed where the medium contains a sufficiently large number of them; pinning down occurs at the cross-over points and at point defects. An increase in the number of dislocations in a solid has the effects of hardening it and rendering it brittle; the number of dislocations in the material may be reduced by annealing.

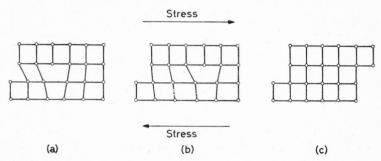

Figure 6.3. Motion of a dislocation through a lattice on the application of a mechanical stress

Attenuation due to dislocations can occur in more than one way (see Mason[3, 10]). For one type of absorption it is assumed that an acoustic wave passing through a crystal sets the dislocations into forced vibrations similar to those for stretched strings. Because of the finite time required for exchanges of energy between the sound waves and the vibrating dislocations, relaxation occurs, the time for which should vary with temperature in accordance with equation 6.7. Bordoni[49] in 1954 investigated this type of absorption in single crystals, using the internal friction method. At frequencies in the lower kilocycle range he measured attenuation in a number of materials at temperatures ranging from 0 to 300° K; his results for copper are given in *Figure 6.4*. For the crystal in its original state damping was small (curve A) but after cold-working there was a considerable increase in attenuation (curve B), and on annealing the specimen a marked decrease in absorption was observed (curve C). It can be seen from the figure that the temperature for maximum attenuation, and hence the relaxation frequency, must be independent of dislocation density. The value of the relaxation frequency for a given temperature is characteristic of the nature of the dislocations but the magnitude of the attenuation depends on the dislocation density.

LOW AMPLITUDE PROPAGATION IN SOLIDS

Another type of attenuation, characteristic of dislocations, has also been observed at kilocycle frequencies. Here the attenuation is proportional to the first power of the frequency, i.e. absorption per cycle is independent of frequency, thus inferring hysteresis losses.

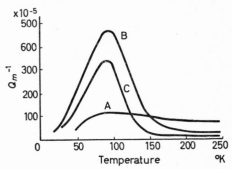

Figure 6.4. Attenuation in copper at 30 kc/s as a function of temperature (after Bordoni[49])

Granato and Lücke[11] suggested that this hysteretic type of loss is caused by the breakaway of the dislocations from their pinning positions by sufficiently high stresses (see *Figure 6.5*). *Figure 6.5a*

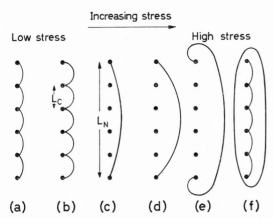

Figure 6.5. Bowing out a pinned lined dislocation under the action of an applied stress (after Granato and Lücke[11])

and *b* show a pinned dislocation line bowed out into loops of length, L_c, under the action of a stress. Where the energy of the applied stress is sufficiently high, the loops break away from the pinning

156

defects to form a fewer number of larger loops of length, L_N (*Figure 6.5c*) and any further increase in stress causes them to bow out (*Figure 6.5d*). On reversing the direction of the stress and then decreasing it, the loops collapse and are again pinned down by the impurities. *Figure 6.6* shows the stress-strain hysteresis loops, for both the ideal and real cases, per half-cycle. The divergence of the shape of the 'real' loop, indicated by the dotted line, from the ideal shape is due to the distribution of values of loop lengths, L_c. *Figure 6.5e* and *f* show that where the stress is sufficiently high, the dislocation loop breaks completely away from the pinning points and a new loop is formed. This mechanism is responsible for fatigue in solid specimens (see Section 8.6). The hysteresis effect just described disappears at high frequencies where there is insufficient time for the loops to respond to the applied stress.

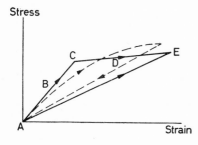

Figure 6.6. Stress-strain hysteresis curves due to dislocation damping. (The solid curve represents the ideal case and the dotted curve corresponds to the 'real' case)

6.5. ABSORPTION IN FERROMAGNETIC AND FERROELECTRIC MATERIALS

Ferromagnetic and ferroelectric materials are composed of 'domains' which are elementary regions characterized by a unique magnetic or electric polarization. These 'domains' are aligned along a number of directions, but generally the polarization vectors are orientated in what are known as 'directions of easy magnetization' (or electrification). These usually follow the direction of the principal crystallographic axes.

Consider a cubic crystal of a ferroelectric material such as iron. There are six directions of easy magnetization lying in positive and negative pairs along the three perpendicular co-ordinate axes. Thus two neighbouring domains will be aligned at angles of either 90 degrees or 180 degrees to one another. Supposing that A and B, or C and D represent two adjacent domains orientated at right-angles to one another (see *Figure 6.7*). Because of the magnetostrictive effect, assuming that the magnetostrictive strain coefficient (see Section 3.9) is positive, there is an increase in length of the domain in the direction of polarization and, because of Poisson's ratio, a decrease in length in a direction at right-angles to this. Thus B and D expand along the X-direction and A and C expand along the Y-direction but contract along the X-direction. There is consequently a displacement of the boundary between two adjacent domains which have their polarizations at right-angles to one another. On the other hand, let P and Q, or R and S represent adjacent domains aligned in opposition, i.e. at 180 degrees to one another. Both P and Q expand along the X-direction so that there is no motion of the boundary between them; the same applies to the domains R and S. Thus there is no displacement of the boundary between two adjacent domains aligned in opposition to one another.

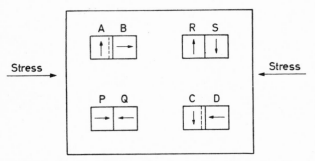

Figure 6.7. Domains in a ferromagnetic or ferroelectric material under stress

Supposing now that a compression is applied along the X-direction. This reduces the existing strain in that direction and increases it in the Y-direction. Hence domains such as A and C grow at the expense of those such as B and D. The boundaries between the domains directed at 90 degrees to one another thus move along the line of the stress. This results in an increase or decrease of the elastic constants, depending on the sign of the magnetostrictive coefficient, the magnitude of the change depending on that of the stress. The phenomenon is called the ΔE *effect*; it occurs also for shear stresses where the domain wall motion is that of rotation, and it can be shown to occur in all types of ferromagnetic and ferroelectric crystals. When a cyclic stress, such as that produced by a sound wave, is applied to a ferromagnetic or ferroelectric material, the domain wall displacement, as a result of the ΔE *effect*, does not vary linearly with the applied stress, but follows a hysteresis loop. There is thus a dissipation of energy, the loss per half-cycle per unit volume being given by the area enclosed by the hysteresis loop, and attenuation increases with strain amplitude and also with frequency. At high frequencies, where the alterations of stress are too rapid for the domain walls to follow, the attenuation disappears. This type of hysteresis loss in ferroelectric transducers such as barium titanate is the cause of their low mechanical Q factors.

Another cause of attenuation in ferromagnetic materials is the production of micro-eddy currents. Eddy currents are induced in the domains by the periodic variations of magnetic flux density, B, as a result of the motion of their walls. For a given domain the magnitude of the induced eddy current is proportional to dB/dt and hence, to ωB_0 at a frequency, $\omega/2\pi$, where B_0 is the flux density amplitude. Because the resultant energy losses are proportional to the square of the induced current, attenuation must increase with the square of the frequency. Eddy currents losses must also increase with electrical conductivity but must decrease for larger domain sizes. At higher frequencies, where the magnetic hysteresis vanishes, there is a decrease in the magnitude of the eddy currents, and absorption from this cause diminishes. Thus there is some frequency, f_0, which corresponds to maximum absorption, and this has been shown by Mason[3] (p. 217) to be given by the expression:

$$f_0 = R/96\chi_0 l^2 \qquad (6.8)$$

where R is the electrical resistivity of the substance, χ_0 its initial magnetic susceptibility, and l the thickness for a plate-like domain. The variation of attenuation with frequency for eddy current losses thus follows that for relaxational type losses.

For a rod of ferromagnetic material, the total loss per cycle, Q_m^{-1} (see equation 2.46a), can be expressed by the equation:

$$Q_m^{-1} = \frac{\Delta Y}{Y_0} \frac{\omega\tau}{1+\omega^2\tau^2} \qquad (6.9)$$

Where $\tau = 1/2\pi f_0$, Y_0 represents the initial Young's modulus and ΔY the maximum change in Young's modulus per cycle. For nickel, domain sizes ranging from 0·2 mm to 0·01 mm correspond to relaxation frequencies extending from 100 kc/s to 50 Mc/s. Very broad attentuation peaks have been obtained experimentally and these indicate a wide distribution of the sizes of the domains.

A fuller account of absorption in ferromagnetic and ferroelectric materials has been given by Mason.[3]

An interesting result of the coupling between acoustic and magnetic energy in ferromagnetic materials was recently observed by Matthews and Le Craw[52] in single crystals of yttrium iron garnet

(YIG). When shear waves were passed along the (100) axis and a sufficiently high magnetic field applied, the polarization of the sound waves was rotated. They used the multiple-echo pulse technique (see Section 6.11) at a frequency of 528 Mc/s and found that the angle of rotation of the wave vector increased in proportion to the path length. Thus the rotation of the nth echo of a given pulse was by an angle of $n\theta$. The value of θ was observed to decrease with increasing field strength.

6.6. ABSORPTION DUE TO ELECTRON-PHONON INTERACTIONS

6.6.1. Attenuation in the Normal State

Debye's theory of specific heats shows that energy exchanges occur in metals between free electrons and the vibrating lattice. Until recently the only way of observing these exchanges has been the study of such physical properties as thermal and electrical conductivities. Bömmel[12] and McKinnon[13] have shown that the measurement of ultrasonic absorption in solids at low temperatures provides an additional tool for investigating these interactions. Debye's theory predicts that the lattice vibrations are quantized in the same way as electro-magnetic vibrations, each quantum being termed a *phonon*, by analogy with the *photon*, which is characteristic of electro-magnetic vibrations. The energy, W, of a phonon is expressed by the relationship:

$$W = hf$$

where h = Planck's constant ($6 \cdot 54 \times 10^{-34}$ joule-sec).

In pure metals, the electron mean free path at room temperatures is of the order of 10^{-6} cm. On reducing the temperature to $1°$ K the mean free path may be increased to as much as $0 \cdot 5$ mm. Consider sound waves at a frequency of 10 Mc/s with a speed of 5,000 metres per sec passing through a metal at a temperature of $1°$ K. Acoustic energy is transmitted by the vibrating lattice, i.e. acoustic phonons. Because the wavelength, $0 \cdot 5$ mm. is of the same order as the electron mean free path, there is a high probability of interactions occurring between the free electrons and the acoustic phonons, which should give rise to absorption of sound waves.

Attenuation of both longitudinal and transverse waves, which can be ascribed to no cause other than this phenomenon, has been observed in a number of metals at temperatures around and below $10°$ K. Bömmel, for example, carried out measurements on lead for a frequency range 9 to 27 Mc/s. He observed an increase in attenuation as the temperature was reduced to $7°$ K, at which superconductivity appears, and then a sudden decrease in attenuation below that temperature (see *Figure 6.8*). Absorption was found to depend on the second power of the frequency and also on the electrical conductivity, and hence on the electron mean free path. Bömmel's observations have been confirmed by later workers for electron mean free paths, l_e, of a lower order than a wavelength ($kl_e < 1$, where $k = 2\pi/\lambda$). Where $kl_e > 1$, it has been observed that, for electrons in the normal state, attenuation is independent of temperature (see *Figure 6.9*) and varies as the first power of the frequency. Mason[14] and Morse[15], working independently of one another, used a free electron model to obtain theoretical expressions of attenuation for $kl_e < 1$.

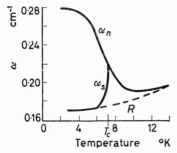

Figure 6.8. Variation of attenuation with temperature for lead (after Bömmel[12])

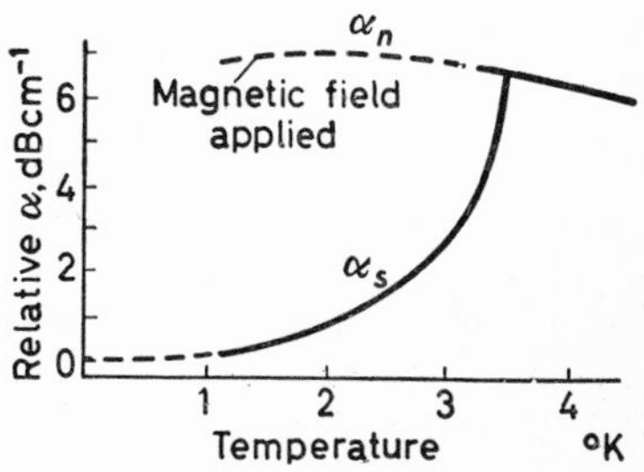

Figure 6.9. Variation of attenuation with temperature for indium at 28·5 Mc/s (after Morse[23])

Morse considered that for an electron gas in a state of equilibrium, the Fermi energy level is the same for all directions, i.e. the Fermi surface is spherical. When the gas is compressed uniformly the Fermi surface remains spherical. The passage of a longitudinal sound wave through the electron gas gives rise to a sudden compression (or rarefaction) in the direction of the wave, and the electron velocity components in that direction react immediately, with the result that the Fermi surface becomes ellipsoidal. Subsequent collisions of the electrons with the lattice tend, in time, to restore the spherical distribution. This is a relaxational phenomenon because the continually varying phase of the sound wave upsets this distribution. Morse found that the absorption coefficient, a, was given by the expression:

$$a = \frac{4}{15} \frac{m E_f \omega^2 \sigma}{e^2 \rho c^3} \qquad (6.10)$$

and the corresponding relaxation time, τ, to be:

$$\tau = \left(\frac{m}{Ne^2}\right)\sigma \qquad (6.11)$$

Here, E_f represents the Fermi energy, σ the electrical conductivity, e the electron charge, m the electron mass, ρ the density of the metal, c the velocity of longitudinal waves, and N the number of electrons per unit volume.

Mason considered that the energy of the electrons in the normal state is carried to and from the lattice vibrations by means of a viscous mechanism, i.e. by transfer of momenta. His analysis, which is easier to follow than that of Morse, is discussed here in more detail.

The viscosity, η, of an ideal gas is given by the equation:

$$\eta = \frac{Nml\bar{v}}{3} \tag{6.12}$$

(see, for example, Champion and Davy[1], p. 181), where l represents the molecular mean free path, $\bar{v}$ the mean molecular velocity, m the molecular mass, and N the number of molecules per unit volume. Expressing these quantities as applying to an electron gas and writing l_e for the electron mean free path, the mean kinetic energy, W, of an electron, obtained from Fermi-Dirac statistics (see e.g. Kittel[9], p. 229) at low temperatures is given by the expression:

$$W = \tfrac{1}{2}m\bar{v}^2 = \frac{3h^2}{10m}\left(\frac{3N}{8\pi}\right)^{\frac{2}{3}} = \frac{3h^2}{40\pi^2 m}(3\pi^2 N)^{\frac{2}{3}} \tag{6.13}$$

The mean free path as determined from electrical conductivity measurements is given by:

$$l_e = \frac{\sigma m\bar{v}}{Ne^2} \tag{6.14}$$

(see e.g. Kittel[9], pp. 237 and 239).

From equations 6.12, 6.13 and 6.14 we obtain:

$$\eta = \frac{h^2 \sigma}{20\pi^2 e^2}(3\pi^2 N)^{\frac{2}{3}} \tag{6.15}$$

For compression waves in a gas it has been shown (see equation 4.12) that:

$$a = \frac{8\pi^2}{3}\left(\frac{\eta}{\rho c^3}\right)f^2 \tag{6.16a}$$

and for shear waves it can easily be shown, using an analysis similar to that for longitudinal waves in Section 4.3.1, that:

$$a_T = 2\pi^2\left(\frac{\eta}{\rho c_T^3}\right)f^2 \tag{6.16b}$$

where c_T represents the shear velocity and a_T the shear attenuation. These give:

$$a = \frac{2}{15} \frac{h^2 \sigma f^2}{\rho c^3 e^2} (3\pi^2 N)^{\frac{2}{3}} \qquad (6.17a)$$

for longitudinal waves, and:

$$a_T = \frac{1}{10} \frac{h^2 \sigma f^2}{\rho c_T^3 e^2} (3\pi^2 N)^{\frac{2}{3}} \qquad (6.17b)$$

for shear waves, i.e.:

$$\frac{a_T}{a} = \frac{3}{4} \left(\frac{c}{c_T}\right)^3$$

Substituting into equation 6.17a the value of the Fermi energy, W_f, as given by the expression:

$$W_f = \frac{h^2}{8\pi^2 m} (3\pi^2 N)^{\frac{2}{3}}$$

(see, for example, Kittel[9], p. 249), we find this equation is identical with the equation 6.10 obtained by Morse.

If we write $W_f = \frac{1}{2}mv_0^2$, where v_0 is the Fermi velocity, and replace $\bar{v}$ by v_0 in equation 6.14, equation 6.17a becomes:

$$a \simeq \frac{2}{15} \frac{Nmv_0\omega}{\rho c^2} kl_e \qquad (kl_e < 1) \qquad (6.18a)$$

and equation 6.17b becomes:

$$a_T \simeq \frac{1}{10} \frac{Nmv_0\omega}{\rho c_T^2} k_T l_e \qquad (k_T l_e < 1) \qquad (6.18b)$$

Pippard in 1955 obtained a general expression for the attenuation of sound waves, with no restriction on the value of kl_e, and equations 6.18 give his values for absorption for the limit where $kl_e < 1$.

For the limit $kl_e > 1$, his expressions are:

$$a \simeq \frac{\pi}{12} \frac{Nmv_0\omega}{\rho c^2} \qquad (kl_e > 1) \qquad (6.19a)$$

for longitudinal waves, and:

$$a_T \simeq \frac{2}{3\pi} \frac{Nmv_0\omega}{\rho c_T^2} \qquad (kl_e > 1) \qquad (6.19b)$$

for shear waves, i.e.:

$$\frac{a_T}{a} = \frac{8}{\pi^2} \left(\frac{c}{c_T}\right)^2$$

6.6.2. Attenuation in the Superconducting State

The earliest observations of Bömmel and McKinnon have shown that a rapid decrease in attenuation takes place at the critical temperature, T_c, for superconductivity. This applies not only when $kl_e < 1$ (*Figure 6.8*) but also when $kl_e > 1$ (*Figure 6.9*). The dotted portions of these curves indicate that attenuation continues to rise with fall of temperature below T_c, when a magnetic field large enough to inhibit the onset of superconductivity is applied. For example (*Figure 6.8*), Bömmel measured attenuation in lead at temperatures ranging from 14° K to 2° K and found that a sudden decrease in absorption occurred at 7° K, which is the value of T_c for lead. With the application of a field of an intensity of 775 oersteds, the normal state was preserved for all temperatures down to 1·5° K.

This variation of attenuation with temperatures in the super-conducting state has been explained by a theory put forward by Bardeen, Cooper and Schrieffer[17] (B.C.S. theory). Fermi-Dirac statistics for a free electron-gas model predict a continuous band of energy levels for electrons in metals. Normally, all the levels below that representing the Fermi energy are occupied by conduction electrons and those above remain unfilled. The application of an electric field or acoustic waves transfers electrons into the unfilled levels. The B.C.S. theory predicts a temperature-dependent energy gap 2ϵ wide around the Fermi level at temperatures of T_c and less. As the temperature is reduced the gap increases in width to a maximum at zero absolute temperature, where the predicted value of ϵ is 1·75 κT_c, κ being Boltzmann's constant. Where $kl_e > 1$ the theory predicts that:

$$\frac{a_s}{a_n} = \frac{2}{\exp. (\epsilon/\kappa T) + 1}$$

where a_s and a_n represent the values of absorption in the super-conducting and normal state, respectively, at a temperature, T. This variation has been confirmed experimentally by Morse and Bohm for indium at 28·5 Mc/s (see *Figure 6.9*). Gibbons and Renton[18] measured the velocities of longitudinal waves in both normal and superconducting tin, and discovered a small reduction in velocity (about 2 parts in 10^6) for the superconducting state.

6.6.3. The Effects of a Magnetic Field on Attenuation

The effect of a magnetic field on a superconducting metal has already been discussed, and in this section the effect on a normal metal is considered. When a magnetic field, H, is applied to a metal at low temperatures, the *cyclotron effect* occurs. Electrons follow circular paths in planes normal to the direction of H with an angular velocity, ω_c, such that:

$$\omega_c = eH/mC$$

164

where e and m represent the charge and mass, respectively, of the electron and C the velocity of light. This results in a change of the electron mean free path and thus affects acoustic attenuation.

Where $kl_e < 1$, a decrease in a has been observed for an increase in H (see *Figure 6.10*). Sternberg[19] has shown with a free electron model

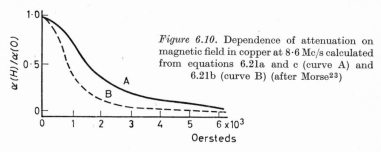

Figure 6.10. Dependence of attenuation on magnetic field in copper at 8·6 Mc/s calculated from equations 6.21a and c (curve A) and 6.21b (curve B) (after Morse[23])

that for shear waves propagated in the x-direction and polarized in the y-direction:

$$a(H) = a(0) \ (1 + \omega_c^2 \tau^2)^{-1} \qquad (6.21a)$$

where H acts in the y-direction,

$$a(H) = a(0) \ (1 + 4\omega_c^2 \tau^2)^{-1} \qquad (6.21b)$$

where H acts in the z-direction,

$$a(H) = a(0) \ (1 + \omega_c^2 \tau^2)^{-1} \qquad (6.21c)$$

where H acts in the x-direction.

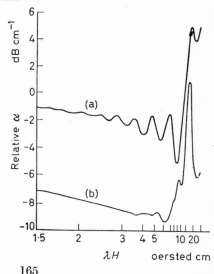

Figure 6.11. Attenuation along (001) direction in copper for longitudinal waves at 75 Mc/s for different values of λH. For curve (a) H is in (100) direction and for curve (b) H is in (110) direction (after Morse and Gavenda[20])

Here $a(H)$ and $a(0)$ represent values of absorption for H being present and absent, respectively, and τ is a relaxation time. These equations agree with experimental measurements. Equation 6.21b has been shown by experiment to hold also for longitudinal waves when the direction of H lies in the yz plane.

Where $kl_e > 1$, i.e. for long mean free paths, $a(H)$ has been observed to vary periodically as the value of H is increased, for both longitudinal and shear waves; *Figure 6.11* illustrates some results

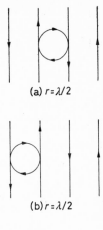

(a) $r = \lambda/2$

(b) $r = \lambda/2$

Figure 6.12. Electron orbits in sound waves. Vertical lines represent the positions of the peak values of the wave vectors

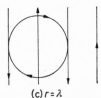

(c) $r = \lambda$

obtained by Morse and Gavenda[20]. This phenomenon was first explained by Pippard[21] and a later theory was put forward by Cohen, Harrison and Harrison[22]. It is best understood by considering its effect on shear waves.

Let shear waves, polarized in the y-direction, be propagated in the x-direction, and let a magnetic field be applied along the z-direction. Circular electron orbits are consequently produced in the xy plane. Because the cyclotron frequency is of the order of 300 times the wave frequency, it can be assumed that the wave is stationary with respect to the electron motion. *Figures 6.12a* and b illustrate electron orbits having diameters equal to one half-wavelength. In *Figure*

6.12a the acoustic wave vectors always lie in the same direction as the motion of the electrons, and the interactions cause the electron velocity to increase. In *Figure 6.12b* the acoustic wave vectors are always in opposition to the electron velocity and there is thus a decrease in the latter. In both these cases there is an increase in current *in phase* with the wave vector, i.e. there is a maximum change in conductivity. This always occurs when the diameter of an electron orbit is equal to an odd number of half-wavelengths. On the other hand, where the diameter is equal to an integral number of wavelengths (see *Figure 6.12c*) there is no net increase or decrease in electron velocity, i.e. the change in conductivity is zero. There is thus a periodic variation in conductivity with the diameter of the electron orbit and, hence, a periodic change in attenuation with magnetic field.

A fuller account of ultrasonic attenuation caused by electron-phonon interactions has been given by Morse[23].

6.7. ABSORPTION IN SINGLE CRYSTALS DUE TO THERMAL EFFECTS

Kittel[24] suggested that acoustic losses caused by thermal conduction might occur in solids and that the value of the corresponding absorption coefficient should be given by equation 4.26, which applies to gases and liquids. This equation predicts very high relaxation frequencies for solids; for metals they may be as high as 50,000 Mc/s. At low temperatures the specific heats of solids are reduced to negligible amounts, in accordance with Debye's theory, and the coefficients of thermal conductivity are much greater than those for room temperatures. One should thus expect considerably reduced values of relaxation frequencies. For tin, for example, at a temperature of $4°$ K, which is just above the critical temperature for superconductivity, the relaxation frequency is only 50 kc/s. However, measurements on metals at low temperatures have yet to yield any satisfactory results for this phenomenon.

Lücke[35] obtained what he considered a more exact expression for thermal conductivity losses in solids but his measurements in materials such as germanium, silicon, and quartz produced absorption coefficients very much higher than his calculated values, even after diffraction losses were considered. The ratios of his measured values of attenuation to the calculated values were of the order of at least 10^3.

Bömmel and Dransfeld[26, 27] measured the attenuation of both longitudinal and shear waves in quartz at frequencies ranging from 1,000 to 4,000 Mc/s, using a hypersonic technique (see Section 6.14), at temperatures between 4° K and 140° K. Their results for longitudinal waves are represented by the curves shown in *Figure 6.13*. Another set of curves resembling these was obtained for shear waves. Their measurements were repeated for the same samples after they were irradiated with neutrons, which had the effect of decreasing the phonon mean free path, and curves following the same pattern but showing a considerable increase in attenuation were obtained.

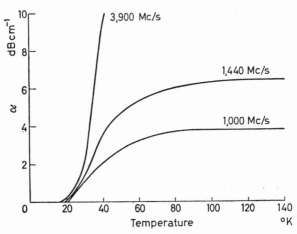

Figure 6.13. Variation of attenuation with temperature for longitudinal waves in quartz (after Bömmel and Dransfeld[26])

This and the fact that the curves resembled the Debye specific heat curves suggested that the observed absorption was of thermal origin.

Similar results to these were obtained for germanium by Dobbs, Chick and Truell[28] at 400 Mc/s and by Verma and Joshi[29] at 508 Mc/s. Furthermore, Lamb, Redwood, and Shteinshleifer[30] found that for a range of frequencies extending from 100 Mc/s to nearly 10,000 Mc/s, the absorption of longitudinal waves in quartz, silicon, germanium and fused silica varied approximately with the second power of the frequency. This indicated that a relaxational process was responsible for the observed attenuation.

Bömmel and Dransfeld suggested that the attenuation which they observed for quartz might be explained by a theory put forward by Akheiser in 1939. This theory postulated that the equilibrium distribution of thermal phonons in a solid may be disturbed by the passage of sound waves, and that the re-establishment of equilibrium is a relaxational phenomenon.

An expression for the absorption coefficient for longitudinal waves in insulating solids was obtained by Woodruff and Ehrenreich[31]. The relaxation time, τ, which they attributed to an Umklapp process, was related to the coefficient of thermal conductivity, K, by the equation:

$$K = \tfrac{1}{3}C_v c^2 \tau \tag{6.22}$$

In this equation C_v represents the molar heat at constant volume and c the average velocity of sound, as given by the Debye relationship:

$$\frac{3}{c^3} = \frac{1}{c_L{}^3} + \frac{2}{c_T{}^3} \tag{5.23}$$

where c_L and c_T represent, respectively, the longitudinal and shear wave velocities in the solid.

Where $\omega\tau \ll 1$ their expression reduces to the equation:

$$\begin{aligned} a &= C_v T \gamma_G{}^2 \omega^2 \tau / 3\rho c^3 \\ &= KT\gamma_G{}^2 \omega^2 / \rho c^5 \end{aligned} \tag{6.24}$$

γ_G in this equation is Grüneisen's constant, which is given by the expression:

$$\gamma_G = a_p V K_S / C_v$$

in which a_p represents the volume coefficient of thermal expansion, V the molar volume, and K_S the adiabatic bulk modulus. Now at temperatures above the Debye temperature K varies inversely with T and hence, KT is constant. Thus a is independent of temperature; this accounts for the levelling of the curves of *Figure 6.13* at higher temperatures. Equation 6.27 also accounts for the observations of Lamb, Redwood, and Shteinshleifer that absorption increases with the square of frequency.

Where $\omega\tau \gg 1$ the expression obtained by Woodruff and Ehrenreich is reduced to the equation:

$$a = \pi \gamma_G{}^2 \omega C_v \tag{6.25}$$

6.8. ABSORPTION DUE TO OTHER POSSIBLE CAUSES

6.8.1. The Acoustoelectric Effect

Weinreich and White[32] passed ultrasonic waves at a frequency of 60 Mc/s through n-type germanium at liquid air temperatures and, as a result, D.C. potential differences of the order of microvolts were observed. These potential differences were attributed to the simultaneous bunching of electrons and 'holes' caused by the passage of sound waves. This effect resembles the thermoelectric effect except that for the latter the phonon frequencies are much higher and are distributed over a continuous range. Blatt[33] showed that the redistribution of free carriers (i.e. electrons and 'holes') by the sound waves is a relaxational phenomenon and should result in absorption. This absorption, however, according to Weinreich, Saunders and White[34] should be small and hence difficult to measure.

6.8.2. Structural Relaxation

Relaxation peaks have been obtained from measurements of absorption coefficients as a function of temperature in glasses such as fused silica, where the molecular arrangements take the forms of random networks. Mason[3] has suggested that the.results obtained were caused by structural relaxation, a phenomenon already discussed in Section 5.2.3.

6.8.3. Thermal Relaxation

Kittel[24] has mentioned the possibility of thermal relaxation of the type discussed in Section 4.4 as being a cause of attenuation in plastics and in rubber-like materials. Richardson[35] (p. 247) has described results of measurements of velocity and attenuation in rubber at frequencies ranging from about 40 kc/s to 3 Mc/s. These clearly indicate the existence of a relaxation phenomenon.

Liebermann[36] put forward a theory in which absorption in organic solids is caused by resonance between the lattice vibrations and the internal vibrations of the molecules of a substance. Results from measurements on solid benzene at 10 Mc/s by Liebermann and on solid cyclohexane for the frequency range, 3 to 8 Mc/s, by Rasmussen[37] have helped to confirm this theory.

6.8.4. Nuclear Magnetic Resonance

Where a substance is subjected to a steady magnetic field, H_0, a number of energy levels associated with the magnetic moments, μ, of its atomic nuclei, appear. The energy difference between two neighbouring levels is equal to $\mu H_0/I$, where I is the nuclear spin quantum number. A transition between these levels is characteristic of a frequency, f_0, as expressed by the relationship:

$$hf_0 = \mu H_0/I$$

where h represents Planck's constant. This transition may be caused by the action of electromagnetic waves of a frequency, f_0, or a harmonic of this frequency; nuclear magnetic resonance is then said to occur.

Nuclear magnetic resonance can also be instigated by ultrasonic waves of frequency, f_0, or a harmonic, and acoustic absorption takes place. For example, attenuation has been observed at about 30 Mc/s in $NaClO_3$ because of the resonance of the Cl nuclei and in InSb at a frequency of nearly 10 Mc/s due to the resonance of the In nuclei. Steady magnetic fields having intensities of the order of 10^3 gauss have been used.

A short account of the use of ultrasonics to investigate this phenomenon has been given by Abragam[38] (p. 417) and the associated theory has been given by Myasnikov.[39]

6.9. PHOTOSENSITIVE ATTENUATION

Nine[40] has reported a change in the attenuation of ultrasonic waves passing through large single crystals of cadmium sulphide as a result of illumination by white light. Hutson, McFee and White[41]

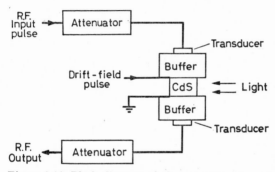

Figure 6.14. Block diagram of the arrangement used by Hutson, McFee, and White[41] for measurements in cadmium sulphide

have shown that where pulsed D.C. electric fields are passed through this substance, when illuminated by white light, amplification of the ultrasonic waves may occur.

Figure 6.14 illustrates the arrangement of the apparatus used by Hutson, McFee and White. The transducers were two similar Y-cut quartz crystals and the buffers, which provided both time delay and electrical insulation, were made of fused silica. The upper and lower surfaces of the cadmium sulphide sample, which was 7 mm thick, were plated with metallic films serving as electrodes. Thus a pulsed D.C. field, called the *drift field*, could be applied in the direction of the sound waves. Pulsed shear waves having frequencies of either 15 Mc/s or 45 Mc/s were passed through the sample. The pulse lengths for the drift field and the sound waves were $5\mu sec$ and $1\mu sec$, respectively and the repetition frequencies for both sets of pulses were the same.

The following results were obtained:

(a) With no illumination and no drift field, acoustic attenuation was low, i.e., 7 dB at 45 Mc/s and 2 dB at 15 Mc/s; the sample displayed insulating properties.

(b) With no illumination but with the drift field acting, no change in attenuation was observed.

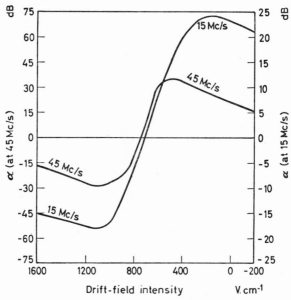

Figure 6.15. Values of a as a function of drift field intensity as obtained by Hutson, McFee, and White[41] for 15 Mc/s $\omega_c/\omega = 1\cdot2$ and for 45 Mc/s, $\omega_c/\omega = 0\cdot21$

(c) With illumination but with no drift field, increases in both attenuation and electrical conductivity were observed as the intensity of illumination was raised.

(d) With both illumination and drift field acting, no change in attenuation was observed unless the time delay was long enough for the drift-field pulse to overlap the acoustic pulse. The attenuation was found to decrease as the amount of overlap increased and, for sufficiently high values of the drift-field intensity, the attenuation decreased to zero and then became negative, i.e. the sound waves were amplified (see *Figure 6.15*).

The gain in amplitude of the ultrasonic waves at ordinary temperatures occurred for a drift field intensity of about 700 volt cm^{-1} for which the drift velocity was equal to the shear wave velocity, about 2,000 m sec^{-1}. This corresponds to a Hall mobility for negative carriers of about 285 cm^2 volt^{-1}, which agrees closely with the value of 300 cm^2 volt^{-1} they obtained from electrical measurements.

Hutson, McFee and White showed that by considering the piezoelectric effect in the specimen for a single carrier species, the value, a, of the absorption coefficient is given by the following expression:

$$a = \frac{\omega}{2c_T} k_c{}^2 \left(\frac{\omega_c/\omega\gamma}{(1 + \omega_c/\omega\gamma)(1 + \omega^2/\omega_c\omega_D)^2} \right) \qquad (6.26)$$

where:
$$\omega_c = \sigma/\epsilon$$
$$\gamma = 1 - v_d/c_T$$
$$\omega_D = c_T{}^2/D$$

Here c_T represents the shear wave velocity, k_c the electromechanical coupling factor as defined by equation 3.19, ω the angular wave frequency, ω_c the angular frequency corresponding to conductivity relaxation, σ the electrical conductivity, ϵ the electrical permittivity, v_d the drift velocity and D the carrier diffusion constant. Fairly good agreement was observed between the measured and the calculated values of a.

6.10. MEASUREMENTS IN SOLIDS

Values of velocities and characteristic impedances for longitudinal waves are, in general, higher for solids than for liquids, but attenuation is usually lower. All the methods which were discussed in Chapter 5 for measuring propagation constants in liquids have been applied to solids with varying degrees of success. One important characteristic of measurements in solids is that it is not possible to vary the acoustic path length for a given specimen. However, a continuous variation of the frequency of the source is more feasible for solids than for fluids, with crystal transducers, because of the heavier damping caused by solid media.

Coupling the transducer to a solid sample for longitudinal waves presents few serious problems provided that the properties of the coupling medium do not vary to any appreciable extent with any physical changes which may take place during an experiment. For example, if the variation of velocity with temperature is measured and a liquid couplant is used, the couplant must retain its liquid state over the whole temperature range. Where measurements are conducted with transverse waves in a solid, the coupling medium must

173

be able to support shear stresses. For this purpose it is usual to employ an adhesive substance, such as phenyl salicylate or canada balsam, which provides a firm bonding but can easily be removed without damaging either the sample or the transducer.

In the following sections the more important techniques for measuring propagation constants in solids are discussed, but for a general survey of the various methods for measuring the elastic properties of solids using ultrasonic methods the reader is referred to McSkimin.[42]

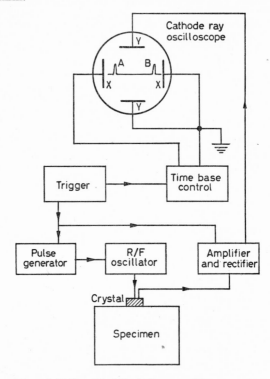

Figure 6.16. Simplified block diagram of the apparatus used for the pulse technique

6.11. THE PULSE TECHNIQUE

The pulse technique, which has been discussed briefly in Section 5.10 in connection with measurements in liquids, is used extensively for determining the propagation constants of solids, especially at megacycle frequencies. *Figure 6.16* depicts a simplified block diagram of the type of apparatus used. The surfaces of the specimen which are normal to the direction of sound propagation should be accurately parallel with one another. For most applications the echo method employing a single reversible transducer is used, but sometimes separate transmitter and receiver crystals are placed at opposite sides of the specimen. Where it is desired to study the detailed wave-form of the pulse the rectifier is not used.

The apparatus is operated by means of a trigger which activates simultaneously the time base control and the pulse generator. At the same time a signal is passed via the amplifier to the Y-plates of the cathode ray oscilloscope; a peak, A, thus appears at the left-hand side of the screen. Triggering occurs at regular intervals with a frequency which may range from about 50 to 1,000 c/s. Where a frequency of 50 c/s is used it is common practice to use the A.C. mains as a trigger. The transmitting crystal is excited at one of its resonant frequencies by means of the radio-frequency oscillator, the output of which is controlled by the pulse generator. In this way, intermittent trains of ultrasonic waves are propagated through the sample. These waves are, in due course, picked up by the receiving crystal and the induced electrical signals are amplified, rectified if necessary, and fed to the Y-plates of the oscilloscope to give the peak, B. Because of the time delay due to the sound pulse travelling through the solid, the peak, B, is displayed further along the time base. Since the time-base frequency is synchronized with the pulse repetition frequency, the peaks, A and B, remain stationary on the screen. Where the time base is calibrated, the time taken for the pulse to travel through the specimen is determined by measuring the distance between A and B. The speed of sound is then obtained by dividing the measured value of the acoustic path length by the time obtained in this way. The time base may be calibrated either by feeding a signal from a standard frequency source to the Y-plates of the oscilloscope or by sending pulses through a material for which the velocity of sound is known.

The attenuation is obtained by measuring the relative heights of the peaks, B, for different path lengths. The path length cannot be varied continuously for solids as it can for liquids but if the time base is contracted sufficiently, a number of equally spaced peaks of decreasing heights, each representing a consecutive reflection, will be observed (see *Figure 6.17*). This method is called the *multiple-echo technique*. Ideally, the peak height should decrease exponentially with distance in the same way as the acoustic amplitude (see equation 2.38b), and the absorption coefficient would be obtained from the logarithmic decrement of the peaks. This operation may be difficult in practice because it is not always possible to ascertain the exact position of the base of any peak. It is more satisfactory to measure the peak decrement with a calibrated attenuator, in the following way. The height of the second or a subsequent peak is adjusted until the summit touches a horizontal line ruled on a graticule placed in front of the screen. The attenuator is then adjusted until the summit of the peak immediately to the left of the one examined touches this line. The fall in the number of dB registered by the attenuator determines the amount of attenuation between each reflection.

The choice of pulse repetition frequency is governed by the absorption coefficient of the material. A high pulse repetition frequency is to be preferred since this provides the maximum degree of brightness for the trace. However, it is essential that a given pulse should be attenuated completely before the next one is propagated otherwise confusion will arise. Thus if, at a given frequency, the absorption coefficient of a material is $0 \cdot 1$ dB cm^{-1}, the acoustic velocity for that material is 5,000 m sec^{-1}, and the maximum signal to noise ratio for the oscilloscope is 100 dB, complete attenuation occurs after $0 \cdot 002$ sec; this corresponds to a pulse repetition frequency of 500 per second.

The choice of pulse length is determined by the nature of the measurement to be made. Where, as for velocity determinations, a high degree of precision is required for the measurement of time, the pulse should be as short as possible. This can be achieved by mounting the transducer for heavy damping, for example, by backing the transducer crystal with a highly absorbent medium and by keeping it in contact with the medium by means of a heavy spring. It is advantageous here to use a transducer such as barium titanate, which has a high coefficient of internal friction, i.e. a low mechanical Q factor, Q_m. However, the heavier the damping the broader the transmitted frequency band as given by equation 2.15a, i.e.:

$$\frac{\Delta\omega}{\omega_r} = Q_m^{-1}$$

where ω_r represents the resonant frequency of the transducer, and $\Delta\omega$ the range of transmitted frequencies for which the corresponding intensities are not less than 3 dB below the intensity at resonance. It can be shown (see Mason[3], p. 100) that the pulse length, P.L., in seconds is given approximately by the expression:

$$\text{P.L.} = \frac{1 \cdot 2 \text{ to } 1 \cdot 4}{\text{band-width in cycles}}$$

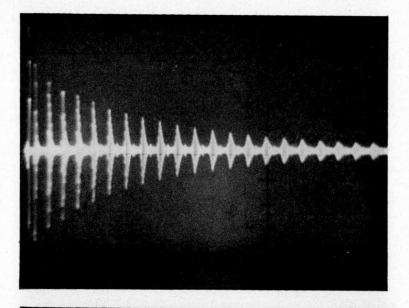

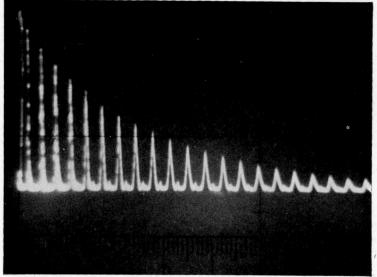

Figure 6.17. Appearance of traces on the screen of the oscilloscope for the multiple-echo pulse method: (*a*) unrectified; (*b*) rectified. Satellite peaks caused by lateral reflections can be seen on these photographs

To face p. 176.

Thus for a transducer having $Q_m = 2$ and radiating at a frequency of 1 Mc/s, the pulse length is about 2·5 μ/sec, which corresponds to 2 complete cycles.

For velocity dispersion and absorption measurements, which are frequency dependent, a narrow bandwidth is essential and longer pulse lengths are required. These can be obtained with an air-backed quartz crystal which is not too heavily clamped to the specimen. The maximum pulse length for pulse-echo methods depends on the thickness of the sample, such that the trailing edge of the pulse

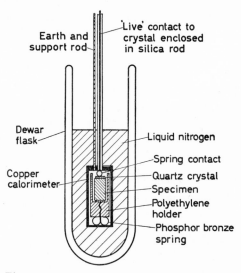

Earth and support rod

'Live' contact to crystal enclosed in silica rod

Dewar flask

Liquid nitrogen

Spring contact

Copper calorimeter

Quartz crystal

Specimen

Polyethylene holder

Phosphor bronze spring

Figure 6.18. Arrangement of a solid specimen in calorimeter as used by the author[43] for measurements of attenuation at different temperatures. (N.B. For the sake of clarity the thermocouple in contact with the specimen has been omitted)

should have left the transducer before the leading edge has returned to it. *Figure 6.18* shows an experimental arrangement based on that of McSkimin[50] and used by the author[43] for measuring absorption coefficients in solids over a wide range of temperatures.

In practice the occurrence of errors with the pulse method may result in the appearance of a non-exponential peak decrement and of spurious peaks on the screen of the oscilloscope (see *Figure 6.17*). These errors may occur as the result of non-parallelism of surfaces, diffraction, and the non-piston like motion of the transducer, as mentioned in connection with the acoustic interferometer (Section

4.11.2). Further inaccuracies may be introduced by a phase change on reflection at the transducer-specimen interface. These errors, however, depend only on wavelength and the dimensions of the specimen and transducer; they remain constant for such determinations as the variation of absorption with temperature, provided that

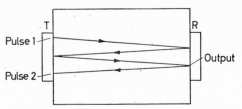

Figure 6.19. Method of Williams and Lamb[44]
for velocity measurements

wavelength changes are negligible. Fuller accounts of errors likely to be encountered with the pulse technique have been given by Morse[23] and McSkimin[42].

Greater accuracy of velocity measurements may be obtained by the use of a null method devised by Williams and Lamb[44], for which a sensitivity of 1 part in 10^4 is claimed. Two similar transducers, one,

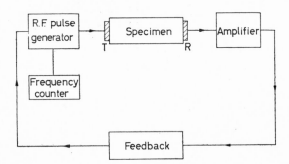

Figure 6.20. Block diagram for the 'sing around' method
(after McSkimin[42])

T (see *Figure 6.19*), acting as transmitter and the other, R, acting as receiver are placed at the opposite ends of the specimen. The pulse repetition frequency is adjusted until the second pulse leaves T at the same time as the first pulse returns to it, after a single reflection at R. Interference thus occurs between the two pulses and

178

cancellation of the signal is obtained by adjusting the wave frequency and the relative amplitudes of the pulses. The time required for the pulses to complete a return journey is thus obtained from the pulse repetition frequency, after suitable corrections for phase changes caused by reflections are made.

Another method which depends on the variation of the pulse repetition frequency is the *sing-around* method, devised by Holbrook and described by McSkimin[42] (see *Figure 6.20*). A pulse from the transmitter, T, is picked up by the receiver, R, and another pulse is then generated by T. The time of travel through the specimen is obtained from the pulse repetition rate as measured by the frequency counter. For absolute velocity measurements, allowance must be made for the time delay in the electrical circuit. This, however, is constant and variations of velocity may be measured without making this correction.

6.12. STATIONARY WAVE METHODS

Stationary wave methods are used extensively for velocity and absorption measurements in solids. They include the interferometer, which has been used for determining velocities over wide ranges of frequency, and *damping capacity* methods which have been employed for attenuation measurements at lower frequencies.

Longitudinal wave velocities at lower megacycle frequencies may be determined by an interferometer method described by Savage[45]. A piezoelectric crystal, mounted for heavy damping and operated below its fundamental resonant frequency, is coupled to a parallel-sided specimen. The crystal frequency is varied continuously and the frequencies for which the crystal response is a maximum are noted. Maximum responses of the crystal occur at the resonant frequencies for thickness vibrations of the specimen. For the nth harmonic the thickness of the specimen is equal to n half-wavelengths. Thus the interval between two adjacent resonances is equal to the fundamental frequency for the specimen, i.e. for a thickness of a half-wavelength.

For the damping capacity method the specimen, in the form of a rod, is mounted at its mid-point between knife-edge or wire supports, and a reversible transducer is applied to one end of the rod. The frequency is varied until fundamental resonance is observed, i.e. when the length of the rod is equal to one half-wavelength. In this way the velocity in the rod can be determined. If the transducer current is switched off the rod executes free damped harmonic vibrations. The logarithmic decrement of these vibrations is obtained by measuring the rate of decrease of the transducer current amplitude

179

and the absorption coefficient is thus determined (see equation 2.38d). Alternatively, the rod may be set into forced vibrations at frequencies in the neighbourhood of resonance and the frequency response curve plotted. Q_m is then obtained from this curve and hence, a. Because of the impracticability of using very short rods this method is usually restricted to frequencies below 100 kc/s. Damping caused by the supports should be reduced to a minimum and the frictional effects of the air are eliminated by mounting the vibrating system *in vacuo*. Bordoni[49], with an electrostatic transducer, used this method for measuring attenuation caused by dislocation damping in solids at low temperatures and at frequencies around 50 kc/s. *Figure 3.23* illustrates an arrangement by Giacomini for such measurements with an electromagnetic transducer. Where a piezoelectric crystal is used it must be cemented to the specimen.

6.13. OTHER METHODS OF MEASUREMENT

6.13.1. Continuous Progressive Wave Methods

Continuous progressive wave methods are not normally possible for solids in bulk because of the difficulty of inserting probe microphones and of eliminating stationary waves. They are, however,

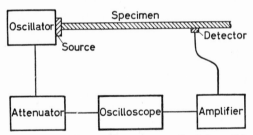

Figure 6.21. Progressive wave method for solids
(after Kolsky[46])

feasible for a solid in the form of a rod or wire, provided that it is sufficiently long and attenuation sufficiently high to prevent the formation of stationary waves; alternatively some form of damping material may be placed at one end. A method for low frequencies, described by Kolsky[46] (p. 142), is illustrated in *Figure 6.21*. The detector, which may be a piezoelectric element, is moved along the rod in which continuous waves are propagated. The source is connected to the X-plates of the oscilloscope and the detector to the Y-plates. The shape of the Lissajous figure (see, for example, Stephens and Bate[16], p. 26) displayed indicates the phase difference corresponding to the relative positions of the detector and source; a change in phase of 360 degrees occurs while the detector is moved through a distance of one wavelength. The velocity is thus obtained if the wave-frequency is known, and attenuation is determined directly from the decrease of amplitude of the Y-component of the figure as the detector is moved.

6.13.2. *Optical, Reverberation and Impedance Methods*

Optical methods of measuring velocities and absorption coefficients have been used for transparent solids at high frequencies. The reverberation method has been employed for solids at lower frequencies. Measurements in rubber-like solids have been conducted with the use of impedance methods, see for example, Mason[3] (p. 115). The physical principles of these methods for solids are the same as those for liquids (see Sections 5.11, 5.12 and 5.13, respectively).

6.13.3. *The Total Reflection Method*

The total reflection method makes use of the principles of reflection and refraction of sound waves at a plane boundary between two media (see Section 2.11.3). For this method the solid is immersed in the liquid and its upper surface forms the plane boundary. Thus medium 1 in *Figure 2.6* represents the liquid and medium 2 the solid. Longitudinal ultrasonic waves are propagated from a crystal transducer along the direction XY, at an angle, θ_1, to the normal, using the pulse technique, and the reflected waves following the path, YW, are received by another transducer. A peak representing the received reflected pulse is displayed on the screen of the oscilloscope.

The angle, θ_1, is increased by rotating the transmitting crystal and the position and orientation of the receiving crystal are adjusted to pick up the maximum amount of energy from the reflected beam. When θ_1 reaches a critical value, for either longitudinal or transverse waves (see *Figure 2.7*) there is a sudden increase in the height of the peak representing the reflected pulse. Provided that the velocity of longitudinal waves in the liquid is known, the velocities of both longitudinal and shear waves in the solid may be calculated from equation 2.62, by putting the angles, θ_2 and θ_2', respectively, equal to 90 degrees.

This method has been used by Mayer[47] at a frequency of 2·5 Mc/s; the critical angles were measured to within 0·9 degree. An advantage of this technique is that only one flat surface of the solid need be used.

6.14. HYPERSONIC WAVES IN SOLIDS

The upper frequency limit for the propagation of ultrasonic waves in solids has been determined by two factors.

(a) Frequencies above 1,000 Mc/s fall within the spectrum of the lattice vibrations of thermal origin. Difficulties arise in that the effect of propagating sound waves of these frequencies through a material is to introduce orderly motion into the thermal phonons in competition with their random motion. These difficulties diminish at low temperatures where the energy of thermal vibrations is low.

(b) Experimental difficulties are encountered when attempting to operate quartz crystals at high harmonic frequencies, because interference is more likely to occur between neighbouring harmonics.

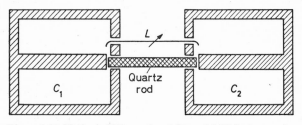

Figure 6.22. Method of Bömmel and Dransfeld[26] for measuring the attenuation of hypersonic waves in quartz

Bömmel and Dransfeld[26] devised a method in which these difficulties were alleviated. They made use of the fact that ultrasonic waves may be excited at the surface of a piezoelectric crystal in contact with an alternating electric field. The wave frequency need not depend on the thickness of the crystal and it can be made as high as the limit attainable with induced electric fields. For one form of the apparatus, shown in *Figure 6.22*, an alternating electric field of the required frequency was applied to the end of a one-inch long quartz rod by means of an electromagnetic microwave cavity resonator, C_1. A similar resonator, C_2, acted as a receiver and a variable electric coupling, L, was provided between the cavities. In this way, waves having frequencies of up to 4,000 Mc/s were propagated in the quartz rod by the pulse method. Attenuation was measured by comparing the response of C_2 to the acoustic waves with calibrated electrical signals passed via the coupling, L. Jacobsen[48] reported having reached an upper frequency limit of 9,370 Mc/s with this method.

REFERENCES

1. CHAMPION, F. C. and DAVY, N. *Properties of Matter*, Blackie, London, 1936
2. REDWOOD, M. *Mechanical Waveguides*, Pergamon, Oxford, 1960

REFERENCES

3. MASON, W. P. *Physical Acoustics and the Properties of Solids*, van Nostrand, New York, 1958
4. BLITZ, J., CLUNIE, D. M., and HOGARTH, C. A. *Proc. Int. Conf. Semiconductor Physics*, Prague, 1961, 641
5. ZENER, C. *Phys. Rev.*, 1938, **53**, 90
6. MASON, W. P. and McSKIMIN, H. J. *J. appl. Phys.*, 1948, **19**, 940
7. HUNTINGDON, H. B. *J. acoust. Soc. Amer.*, 1950, **22**, 362
8. COTTRELL, A. H. *Dislocations and Plastic Flow in Crystals*, Oxford University Press, 1953
9. KITTEL, C. *An Introduction to Solid State Physics*, 2nd Edn., Wiley, New York/Chapman and Hall, London
10. MASON, W. P. *Bell System Tech. Journal*, 1955, **34**, 903
11. GRANATO, A. and LÜCKE, K. *J. appl. Phys.*, 1956, **27**, 583
12. BÖMMEL, H. E. *Phys. Rev.*, 1954, **96**, 220
13. McKINNON, L. *Phys. Rev.*, 1955, **98**, 1181
14. MASON, W. P. *Phys. Rev.*, 1955, **97**, 557
15. MORSE, R. W. *Phys. Rev.*, 1955, **97**, 1716
16. STEPHENS, R. W. B. and BATE, A. E. *Wave Motion and Sound*, Arnold, London, 1950
17. BARDEEN, J., COOPER, L. N. and SCHRIEFFER, *Phys. Rev.*, 1957, **108**, 1175
18. GIBBONS, D. F. and RENTON, C. A. *Phys. Rev.*, 1959, **114**, 1257
19. STERNBERG, M. S. *Phys. Rev.*, 1958, **110**, 772
20. MORSE, R. W. and GAVENDA, J. D. *Phys. Rev. (L)*, 1959, **3**, 250
21. PIPPARD, A. B. *Phil. Mag.*, 1957, **2**, 1147
22. COHEN, M. H., HARRISON, M. J. and HARRISON, W. A. *Phys. Rev.*, 1960, **117**, 937
23. MORSE, R. W. *Progress in Cryogenics* (ed. K. Mendelssohn), Vol. I, Heywood, London, 1959
24. KITTEL, C. *Rep. Prog. Phys.*, 1948, **11**, 232
25. LÜCKE, K. *J. appl. Phys.*, 1956, **27**, 1433
26. BÖMMEL, H. E. and DRANSFELD, K. *Phys. Rev. (L)*, 1958, **2**, 288
27. BÖMMEL, H. E. and DRANSFELD, K. *Phys. Rev.*, 1960, **117**, 1245
28. DOBBS, E. R., CHICK, B. B. and TRUELL, R. *Phys. Rev. (L)*, 1959, **3**, 332
29. VERMA, G. S. and JOSHI, S. K. *Phys. Rev.*, 1961, **121**, 396
30. LAMB, J., REDWOOD, M. and SHTEINSHLEIFER, *Phys. Rev. (L)*, 1959, **3**, 28
31. WOODRUFF, T. O. and EHRENREICH, H. *Phys. Rev.*, 1961, **123**, 1553
32. WEINREICH, G. and WHITE, H. G. *Phys. Rev.*, 1957, **106**, 1104
33. BLATT, F. J. *Phys. Rev.*, 1957, **105**, 1118
34. WEINREICH, G., SAUNDERS, T. M. and WHITE, H. G. *Phys. Rev.*, 1959, **114**, 33
35. RICHARDSON, E. G. *Ultrasonic Physics*, 2nd Edn., Elsevier, Amsterdam, 1962
36. LIEBERMANN, L. *Phys. Rev.*, 1959, **113**, 1052
37. RASMUSSEN, R. A. *J. acoust. Soc. Amer.*, 1960, **32**, 774
38. ABRAGAM, A. *The Principles of Nuclear Magnetism*, O.U.P., 1961

39. MYASNIKOV, L. L. *Soviet Physics, Acoustics*, 1961, **6**, 347
40. NINE, H. N. *Phys. Rev. (L)*, 1960, **6**, 359
41. HUTSON, A. R., MCFEE, J. H. and WHITE, D. L. *Phys. Rev. (L)*, 1961, **7**, 237
42. MCSKIMIN, H. J. *J. acoust. Soc. Amer.*, 1961, **33**, 606
43. BLITZ, J. *Brit. J. Non-Destructive Testing*, 1960, **2**, 62
44. WILLIAMS, J. and LAMB, J. *J. Acoust. Soc. Amer.*, 1958, **30**, 308
45. SAVAGE, F. M. *J. Brit. Instn. Radio Engrs.*, 1954, **14**, 456
46. KOLSKY, H. *Stress Waves in Solids*, Oxford University Press, 1953
47. MAYER, W. G. *J. acoust. Soc. Amer.*, 1960, **32**, 1213
48. JACOBSEN, E. K. *Phys. Rev. (L)*, 1959, **3**, 249
49. BORDONI, P. G. *J. acoust. Soc. Amer.*, 1954, **26**, 495
50. MCSKIMIN, H. J. *J. appl. Phys.*, 1953, **24**, 988
51. KAYE, G. W. C. and LABY, T. H. *Tables of Physical and Chemical Constants*, 11th Edn., Longmans, Green, London, 1957
52. MATTHEWS, H. and LE CRAW, R. C. *Phys. Rev. (L)*, 1962, **8**, 397

7

LOW POWER APPLICATIONS OF ULTRASONICS

7.1. GENERAL CONSIDERATIONS

THE techniques used for measuring acoustic velocities and absorption coefficients, as described in the previous chapters, have been developed to a considerable extent in their applications to industry, research, and medical practice. For example, velocity measurement methods have been adapted to such purposes as the location of defects in materials, thickness gauging, the determination of elastic constants and estimating concentrations of solutions. Techniques used for measuring absorption have been applied to such purposes as estimating degrees of hardness of metals, determining grain sizes in polycrystalline materials, measuring pressures of gases, and distinguishing malignant from healthy tissue in living matter. In this chapter a selection of the more important applications already in common use, or likely to be adopted in the near future, is given. Further details of low-power applications have been described by Carlin,[1] Crawford[2] and Glickstein,[3] and latest developments are currently described in *Ultrasonic News*, the *Non-destructive Testing Journal*, and the *British Journal of Non-Destructive Testing*.

7.2. FLAW DETECTION AND THICKNESS GAUGING

Ultrasonics were first used for flaw detection by Sokolov in 1934, who used a simple image converter method (see Section 7.5). This technique was crude and had little practical application. Not much progress was made in this direction until the development of the pulse technique (see Section 6.11). In general, longitudinal waves are used and, where possible, the single probe pulse-echo method is usually employed. This consists of passing a pulsed beam of ultrasonic waves through the specimen from a reversible transducer placed on one surface. The beam is then reflected from the opposite surface, or a defect, back to the transducer.

The use of the single probe pulse-echo method for flaw detection is straightforward where the specimen has two parallel surfaces, and the defect is a linear one roughly parallel with them but not too

185

close to them or to another defect. In the absence of any defect, two peaks, A and B, appear on the screen of the oscilloscope, see *Figure 6.16*. A represents the instant of transmission of the pulse and B that of its return after a single echo. The peak, B, is often said to represent the *bottom echo*. Where a defect is present, a discontinuity of characteristic impedance occurs and some or all of the sound energy is reflected back to the transducer. This results in the appearance of another peak, C, between A and B. The distance, AC, determines the depth of the flaw, and the height of the peak, C, indicates the extent of the defect.

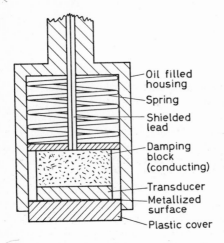

Oil filled housing
Spring
Shielded lead
Damping block (conducting)
Transducer
Metallized surface
Plastic cover

Figure 7.1. Schematic diagram of longitudinal wave probe

For flaw detection a crystal transducer is normally used. This is located in a suitable housing and the complete arrangement is called a *probe* (see *Figure 7.1*). The crystal is mounted for heavy damping; this results in the propagation of short pulses so that greater accuracy is obtained in locating defects and in the resolution of neighbouring defects from one another. To prevent wear from friction between the surfaces of the crystal and the material under test, the transducer is often protected with a plastic cover, e.g. Perspex or PVC, which is coupled to the crystal with oil. Ideally the characteristic impedances of the transducer substance, the material of the protective cover, and the oil should be similar. Although the probe is usually coupled to the specimen with a liquid film, it is sometimes more desirable to use the *immersion technique*. For this method both the test sample and the probe are immersed in water with the probe at a fixed distance from the upper surface of the sample. An additional peak, which represents the echo from the interface between the

Figure 7.2a. Wedge and variable angle probes (*courtesy of Ultrasonoscope, Ltd., London*)

To face p. 186.

immersing liquid and the sample, appears on the screen of the oscilloscope.

Where a defect is not parallel with the surface it is better to use an *angled-probe,* which consists of a transducer mounted on a wedge (see *Figure 7.2a*). This enables sound waves to be incident normally to the defect and a greater degree of sensitivity is achieved. The use of *variable-angle probes* (see *Figure 7.2a*) enables one to estimate the directions of defects and also indicates the positions of awkwardly situated flaws, which might remain undetected with an ordinary probe (see *Figure 7.2b*).

Two probes, one acting as a sender and the other as a receiver, are often used for the location of defects in samples having irregular shapes and for detecting flaws at a depth of the order of or less

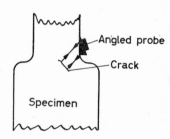

Figure 7.2b. Location of awkwardly placed defect with angled probe

than a pulse length. Care must be taken to ensure that coupling between the transducers, other than through the medium, does not occur.

Flaws, such as defects in butt-welds, orientated at right-angles to the surface are commonly detected by *forward scanning* for which a beam of transverse waves is propagated, after mode conversion, in the medium at a shallow angle to the surface. The transducer is mounted on a Perspex wedge (see *Figure 7.3*) and longitudinal waves are directed to the surface with an angle of incidence greater than the first critical angle (see Section 2.11.3). The diagram shows an extension to the wedge shaped in such a way that longitudinal waves which are reflected at the surface are completely absorbed by subsequent reflections. A similar probe placed in a suitable position (see *Figure 7.4*) receives the waves reflected from the defect after a further reflection at the base of the sample. Because, for a given substance, the transverse wave velocity is about half the longitudinal wave velocity, the sensitivity of this method is double that of longitudinal wave techniques.

Surface defects have been detected by means of surface waves, which may be produced by a probe similar in design to that illustrated in *Figure 7.3*. The incident longitudinal beam is directed to the surface at the second critical angle so that transverse waves are refracted at an angle of 90 degrees, i.e. along the surface. Laminar defects just below the surface, which may be difficult to detect by

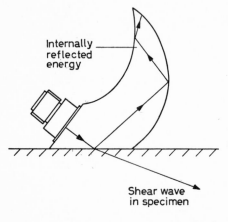

Internally
reflected
energy

Shear wave
in specimen

Figure 7.3. Design of transverse wave probe (after Sproule and Wells[13]) (*courtesy of Ultrasonoscope Ltd., London*)

normal longitudinal wave methods, have been located by Lamb waves.[4] Lamb showed that a solid plate can resonate at an infinite number of frequencies; the portion of the sample between the surface and a lamination close to it forms such a plate and, if surface waves are directed towards this plate, it will resonate and cause an indication to appear on the screen of the oscilloscope.

Figure 7.4. Use of transverse wave probes to locate a defect in a butt-weld.

Receiver   Transmitter   Defect

Flaw detection by ultrasonics requires a considerable amount of skill on the part of the operator who, with suitable training, should be able to identify different types of defects from the configurations of the traces on the screen of the oscilloscope. Great care must be taken to ensure that such a trace does correspond to an actual defect. Spurious traces may occur, for example, as a result of beam spreading and reflection from the sides of the sample, accompanied perhaps by mode conversion (see Section 2.11.3). Furthermore it may happen that a defect occurs in a position of minimum intensity in the Fresnel zone (see Section 2.12), with the result that no trace or only a small trace appears.

Where the pulse technique is used for thickness gauging, better results are obtained by the use of a variable delay line (see Section 7.3). Simultaneous with the propagation of the pulse in the sample another pulse is sent through the delay line, which may be a length of nickel wire (see *Figure 7.7*) or a column of liquid terminated by a reflector. The received pulse is indicated on the screen of the oscilloscope by a trace additional to that representing the pulse propagated in the sample. The delay line is adjusted in length by means of a micrometer device until the two traces on the screen coincide in position; the thickness of the specimen is then obtained from the calibration of the delay line. Thickness gauging may also be conducted using the resonance method described in Section 6.12.

An important advantage of ultrasonic methods for thickness measurement is that access to only one surface of the sample is necessary. This is especially useful for measuring the extent of corrosion inside pipes. Thicknesses of the hulls of ships can be measured from the inside whilst at sea, thus avoiding the expensive and time consuming process of taking sample borings in dry dock, a method which is not 100 per cent effective. Another interesting application of ultrasonic thickness gauging is the measurement of the depths of fat on the bodies of live animals. This has proved extremely valuable to the pig industry.

A fuller account of ultrasonic and other methods of the non-destructive testing of materials has been given elsewhere.[5, 14-16]

7.3. ULTRASONIC DELAY LINES

Delay lines are devices for storing electrical signals for finite time periods. They are particularly used in computers for storing information to be extracted at a later stage of a calculation. One method is to convert these signals into ultrasonic waves and, after their having travelled a given distance through a material, to reconvert them into their original forms.

The simplest form of ultrasonic delay line consists of a crystal transducer radiating into a column of liquid, such as mercury, terminated by a reflector. The delay time may be adjusted by altering the position of the reflector relative to the crystal. Liquid delay lines are not always convenient to use and solid lines are more common. For delay times of the order of microseconds it is sufficient to place transducers at either end of a solid rod or block a few centimetres long. The delay time may be doubled by using shear waves and *Figure 7.5* illustrates a device in which these are produced by mode conversion. Where delay times of the order of milliseconds are required, very long acoustic paths are necessary. These can be obtained by using materials in the forms of polygons for which large numbers of multiple reflections occur (see *Figure 7.6*). Great care is demanded for the design of a polygon because trouble from diffraction and unwanted mode conversion must be avoided.

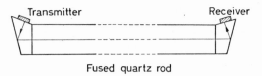

Fused quartz rod

Figure 7.5. Delay line using shear waves produced by mode conversion (after May[18])

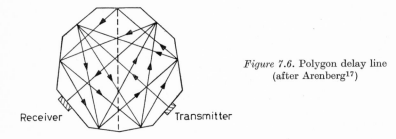

Figure 7.6. Polygon delay line (after Arenberg[17])

A disadvantage of the solid delay lines described above is that the delay time cannot be varied. Furthermore, unless a highly attenuating medium is used, unwanted signals may occur as a result of reflections subsequent to the end of the required delay. This may be

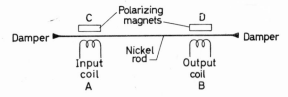

Figure 7.7. Magnetostrictive delay line

turned to advantage where the device is also required as a time marker. The magnetostrictive type of delay line, such as the one illustrated in *Figure 7.7*, can be varied in length and unwanted reflections are avoided by covering the ends of the rod with grease, which completely absorbs the sound waves. The line consists of a rod, wire, or ribbon of some ferromagnetic material such as nickel.

An electrical signal applied to the coil, A, induces a sound pulse in the line by the magnetostrictive effect. When this arrives at the coil, B, the sound waves induce an electrical signal in it by the converse magnetostrictive effect. Permanent magnets, C and D, provide the necessary polarization (see Section 3.8).

Further information about ultrasonic delay lines has been given by Mason[6] and in a number of articles appearing in the I.R.E. transactions on *Ultrasonic Engineering*, New York, June 1960, Vol. UE-7, No. 2.

7.4. MEASUREMENTS OF MECHANICAL STRESSES

When a medium is subjected to a mechanical stress, changes occur in its elastic moduli and hence in its acoustic velocities. Shahbender[7] described how it is possible to measure stresses exerted on a body by their effects on ultrasonic velocities. This method should prove extremely valuable because it determines variations of stress with time.

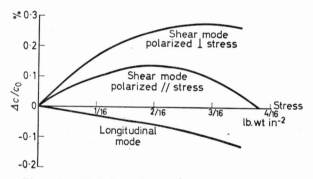

Figure 7.8. Variations of acoustic velocity with applied stress (after Shahbender[7])

Before measurements are possible for a given material it is necessary to obtain calibration curves. These consist of plots of the variations of percentage velocity with applied stress in a direction perpendicular to the latter. *Figure 7.8* illustrates calibration curves for longitudinal waves and also for shear waves polarized both perpendicular to and parallel with the direction of the stress. It is seen that the variations of the two components of shear velocity with time are different; thus at any given time the corresponding wave vectors are out of phase with one another. The phase difference, ϕ, is given by the expression:

191

$$\phi = \frac{\omega l}{c_0}\left[\left(\frac{\Delta c}{c_0}\right)_n - \left(\frac{\Delta c}{c_0}\right)_p\right]$$

Here ω represents the angular frequency, l the acoustic path length, c_0 the shear wave velocity in the unstrained medium, and $\left(\frac{\Delta c}{c_0}\right)_n$ and $\left(\frac{\Delta c}{c_0}\right)_p$ the fractional shear wave velocity for polarizations in directions perpendicular to and parallel with the direction of stress respectively.

The value of the applied stress is thus determined from ϕ and l as obtained by the pulse technique. The value of l is obtained simply from longitudinal wave measurements; ϕ is measured in the following manner. Two similar Y-cut crystal transducers acting as transmitters are mounted one above the other on the surface of the medium with the directions of their vibrations (i.e. the X-axes) respectively parallel with and perpendicular to the direction of application of the stress. A delay network brings about a phase difference of 90 degrees between the vibrations, so that the wave vector is circularly polarized on propagation. Because the waves travel at different speeds the polarization is generally elliptical. The components of the ellipse are picked up by the receiver and the value of ϕ is obtained by means of a suitable phase-shift network.

7.5. ULTRASONIC IMAGE CONVERTERS

For an ultrasonic image converter a solid sample is immersed in a liquid and 'illuminated' by ultrasonic waves. The sample then acts as an object for an acoustic lens system and an image is formed in the same way as for an optical system. The acoustic image is then converted to an optical image of the sample. In this way the interior of an optically opaque object can be examined. The whole system is immersed in a liquid to obtain an efficient acoustic coupling.

For one method, described by Pohlman (see Hueter and Bolt[8], p. 353), the image converter consisted of a thin cell containing a liquid in which were suspended a large number of minute aluminium discs having diameters small compared with wavelength. These discs were orientated initially in a direction normal to the sound waves and behaved as Rayleigh discs (see Section 3.15.3) when irradiated, their angles of rotation depending on the acoustic pressure. Thus when the cell was illuminated optically a visual image of the sample appeared.

Sokolov, in 1950, described a system in which the image converter was an electronic scanning tube; this is now being further developed in England by Smyth and Sayers.[9] The object, O (see *Figure 7.9*) was immersed in a tank of water and 'illuminated' by ultrasonic waves from the quartz crystal, C. Images of points in O were focussed by the lens, L, on to the quartz plate, Q, which formed the end boundary of the cathode ray tube, T, replacing the usual fluorescent screen. The action of the ultrasonic waves on Q was to produce varying electric charges over its opposite surfaces by the piezoelectric effect. Q was, at the same time, bombarded by a narrow beam of cathode rays which scanned the surface systematically in the manner of a television scanner, and secondary electrons were given off and collected by the anode, A. The anode current was amplified and fed to a modulator connected to the cathode in another cathode ray tube, of conventional design. The fluorescent screen of this tube was scanned by a modulated cathode beam in phase with

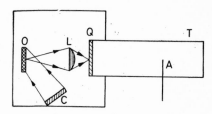

Figure 7.9. Ultrasonic image converter arrangement of Sokolov

the scanning in the first tube. In this way an optical image could be observed on the screen of the second tube.

The resolving power of the system is dependent upon wavelength and the aperture size of the image converter. In water, wavelengths as low as 5×10^{-5} cm would occur for frequencies of the order of 3,000 Mc/s. Wavelengths of this order overlap those of visible light and resolving powers similar to those obtained for optical instruments should then be possible.

A simple but crude image converter based on the one originally used by Sokolov in 1934 (see Glickstein[3], p. 124) may be obtained by immersing the object in the bath of a vertical ultrasonic beam in water. An acoustic lens is placed above the object so that an image is formed on the liquid surface. This is made visible by means of an oblique beam of light incident to the surface.

7.6. THE ULTRASONIC DIFFRACTION GRATING

In Section 5.11.3 it was shown that when a beam of ultrasonic waves crosses a transparent medium, the resultant compressions and rarefactions form an optical diffraction grating. Because the grating is switched on and off at twice the frequency of the sound waves this device can be used as a stroboscope. Houstoun in 1941 used this method for the measurement of the velocity of light. Stationary waves of a frequency of 100 Mc/s were produced in a quartz crystal so that a grating appeared intermittently at a frequency of 200 Mc/s. A beam of monochromatic light through the crystal was blocked on the far side by a screen in which was cut an aperture which allowed only the first order diffracted rays to pass through. The beam was reflected back along its original path by a mirror placed at a measured distance from the crystal. This distance was adjusted until the reflected beam arrived back at the grating at the instant the latter was switched off. Thus the time taken for the diffracted beam to proceed on its forward and return journey between the crystal and the reflector was a multiple of one quarter of the time period of the ultrasonic waves. The velocity of light was determined by observing two consecutive positions of the reflector for complete interruption of the reflected beam.

It was also pointed out in Section 5.11.3 that the distribution of the intensities in the diffracted optical beam is dependent on the acoustic intensity and that the intensity of the zeroth order spectrum decreases as the acoustic intensity increases. This indicates that the ultrasonic grating can be used for the modulation of light waves and that it can also be used as an image converter (see Section 7.5). Bergmann[10] (p. 191) has described an application of this phenomenon to a television system.

7.7. UNDERWATER APPLICATIONS

Marine applications of ultrasonics date back to the 1914–18 war when they were used for the location of submarines. Considerable advances have since been made in this field with the pulse technique and ultrasonic waves are now commonly used for sounding ocean beds. With an automatic pen recorder one can obtain a recorded profile of the ocean bed on a chart as a result of reflected pulses being received. It is also possible to locate shoals of fish by this method and it has been claimed that a given fish species can be identified from the characteristics of the recorded traces. Because of the long path lengths in sea water, frequencies in the lower kilocycle range must be used to avoid too high an attenuation.

Signalling is another underwater application of ultrasonics. With ultrasonic waves as a carrier, modulation devices enable the transmission of speech between ships.

7.8. ULTRASONIC APPLICATIONS IN AIR

At present there are not many ultrasonic applications in open air and these are restricted to the lower kilocycle range, where attenuation is not too great. One of these which has met with some success is an intruder alarm system for the detection of burglars and fire in enclosed premises. A magnetostrictive transducer is placed at some point in a room and the pulses are propagated in all directions. These are reflected by the walls and furniture and eventually picked up by a receiver, from which a constant indication is obtained. Any variation in the sound field, caused by an intruder or increase in temperature, gives rise to a change in this indication, which sets off an alarm.

Another application of airborne ultrasonics is a system for the guidance of blind people. It consists of sending out ultrasonic pulses which are reflected by objects in the vicinity. Where these objects are moving a change of frequency occurs due to the Doppler effect (see Section 2.15), i.e. a receding object causes a drop in frequency and an advancing object an increase in frequency. This work is still in the experimental stage but there is every hope of success in view of the fact that bats which are totally blind rely on ultrasonics for their navigation. When flying at high speeds they can find their homes after journeys of as long as fifty miles.

7.9. THE ULTRASONIC VISCOMETER

In Section 5.5 it was shown that the attenuation of shear waves in a viscous liquid at a given frequency decreases with increasing viscosity. Thus the damping of a shear wave transducer vibrating in such a liquid is a function of the coefficient of viscosity of the liquid. One method of measuring this quantity is to apply a pulse to a Y-cut crystal or to a torsionally vibrating rod immersed in the liquid so that it vibrates freely with damped harmonic motion. When the amplitude of the vibrations falls to a predetermined level another pulse is generated. Thus the pulse repetition frequency increases with damping and hence decreases with increase in viscosity. The device is calibrated using liquids having known coefficients of viscosity.

7.10. THE ULTRASONIC FLOWMETER

The ultrasonic flowmeter operates on the Doppler principle (see Section 2.15). Two reversible transducers are placed in the liquid along the line of flow, one acting as transmitter and the other as receiver using the pulse technique. At short regular intervals they are switched over so that the transmitter becomes a receiver and the receiver a transmitter. The velocities are $c + u$ along the direction of flow and $c - u$ in the reverse direction, where c represents the acoustic velocity and u the velocity of the streamline flow of the liquid.

Peaks corresponding to these velocities appear on the screen of an oscilloscope and, because the frequency of switching over the transducers is high, the two peaks are observed simultaneously. The distance between the peaks determines the velocity of flow of the liquid.

7.11. PRESSURE MEASUREMENTS IN FLUIDS

In Section 3.42 it was shown that the amplitude of the vibrations of a piezoelectric crystal is dependent upon the radiation impedance R_m, of the medium in which it is placed. For plane waves this is given by:

$$R_m = \rho c A$$

where A represents the area of the radiating surface, ρ and c the density and velocity of sound, respectively, for the medium. When the pressure of a non-dispersive gas is varied at constant temperature only ρ varies, in accordance with Boyle's law, and c remains constant. It is then possible to measure the pressure of the gas at a given temperature from the response of the crystal vibrations.

Pacey[11] devised a manometer in which a quartz crystal was mounted in a gas or vapour and maintained in vibration by means of a Pierce type of circuit, similar to that illustrated in *Figure 3.2*. Variations in amplitude, as indicated by changes in anode current, were registered on a suitable meter which could be calibrated in units of pressure.

7.12. MEDICAL APPLICATIONS

The techniques used for flaw detection (see Section 7.2) have been extended with a considerable degree of success to medical diagnosis. The characteristic impedances and absorption coefficients of different parts of the human body, such as fat layers, muscle, bone, etc., vary sufficiently to render these methods highly successful. It has also been found that the acoustic properties of healthy and malignant tissue differ to such an extent that an early diagnosis of cancer is sometimes possible. Care must be taken to ensure that the acoustic powers used are not high enough to cause damage to the body either by heating or by cavitation.

Frequencies in the lower megacycle range are commonly used and coupling is normally achieved by the immersion technique. One method is to use water contained in a vessel having a rubber bottom, which can be placed in contact with the skin. Scanning is achieved by moving the transducer inside the vessel.

Transmission techniques are often used, especially for the diagnosis of brain tumours. A method devised by Hueter and Bolt[12]

196

makes use of the apparatus illustrated in *Figure 7.10*. The transducers are vertical barium titanate strips, one acting as transmitter and the other as a receiver, connected together by a rigid support so that they remain in line when moved. These transducers are immersed in water throughout the measurements. The strips are divided into twenty sections so that scanning in the vertical direction is carried out by switching them into the circuit in turn by means of a commutator. At the end of each vertical scan the transducer support is moved a

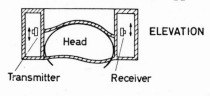

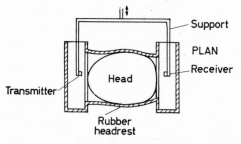

Figure 7.10. Apparatus used for ultrasonic brain examination (after Hueter and Bolt[12])

short distance horizontally and in this way a complete survey of the head can be made. The presence of malignant growths is indicated by abnormal values of attenuation. The frequency used by Hueter and Bolt was 2·5 Mc/s and the upper limit of power was 1 watt.

Examinations of the heart have been conducted by means of a Doppler technique. Ultrasonic waves are directed towards the heart and reflected back again. The velocity of the walls of the heart is determined by the observed change in frequency (see equation 2.70). Any irregularities from normal functioning can readily be detected.

The ultrasonic flowmeter discussed in Section 7.10 has also been used successfully for the measurement of the rate of flow of blood through the human body.

7.13. MISCELLANEOUS APPLICATIONS

Other applications of low power ultrasonics include the determination of the temperature of a gas by measuring its acoustic velocity and the detection of impurities in gases from measurements of their absorption coefficients (see Section 4.8). One ingenious device is the use of a crystal transducer for maintaining a constant liquid level in a tank. When the transducer is immersed the acoustic load on it is greater than when it lies above the liquid level. The change in crystal current due to the variation of the acoustic load caused by a change in level is used to operate a tap in the liquid supply line.

REFERENCES

1. CARLIN, B. *Ultrasonics*, 2nd Edn., McGraw-Hill, New York, 1960
2. CRAWFORD, A. E. *Ultrasonic Engineering*, Butterworths, London, 1955
3. GLICKSTEIN, C. *Basic Ultrasonics*, Rider, New York/Chapman and Hall, London, 1960
4. WORLTON, D. C. *Nondestr. Test.*, 1957, **15**, 218
5. HOGARTH, C. A. and BLITZ, J. (eds.) *Techniques of Non-Destructive Testing*, Butterworths, London, 1960
6. MASON, W. P. *Physical Acoustics and the Properties of Solids*, van Nostrand, New York, 1958
7. SHAHBENDER, R. A. *Trans. I.R.E.*, 1961, **UE-8**, 19
8. HUETER, T. F. and BOLT, R. H. *Sonics*, Wiley, New York/Chapman and Hall, London, 1955
9. SMYTH, C. N. and SAYERS, J. F. *J. Instn. Elec. Engnrs.*, 1959, **5**, 262
10. BERGMANN, L. *Ultrasonics* (trans. H. S. Hatfield), Wiley, New York/Bell, London, 1938
11. PACEY, D. J. *Vacuum*, 1959/60, **9**, 261
12. HUETER, T. F. and BOLT, R. H. *J. acoust. Soc. Amer.*, 1951, **23** 160
13. SPROULE, D. O. and WELLS, L. H. *S and T Memo*, 19/55, Ministry of Supply, 1955
14. CHALMERS, B. and QUARRELL, A. G. *The Physical Examination of Metals*, 2nd Edn., Arnold, London, 1960
15. McMASTER, R. C. (ed.) *Nondestructive Testing Handbook* (2 vols.), Ronald, New York, 1960
16. STANFORD, E. G. and FEARON, J. H. (eds.) *Progress in Non-Destructive Testing*, Vols. 1, 2 and 3, Arnold, London, 1958 and 1962, respectively
17. ARENBERG, D. L. *Ultrasonic Delay Lines*, I.R.E. Conv. Record, 1954
18. MAY, J. E. *Trans. I.R.E.*, 1956, PGUE, **4**, 3

HIGH ENERGY ULTRASONIC WAVES

8.1. GENERAL CONSIDERATIONS

HIGH energy ultrasonic waves may be regarded as those for which there is no longer a linear relationship between the applied stress and the resultant strain. These waves will have some effect on the medium through which they pass. In this chapter the more important of their effects are discussed and some applications which have proved successful or show promise of success are described. For greater detail the reader is referred to Crawford[1] and the other authors mentioned in the text.

8.2. CAVITATION

Cavitation is a phenomenon which is observed in boiling water and also in sea water, in the vicinity of a rotating ship's propeller. It occurs in those regions of a liquid which are subjected to rapidly alternating pressures of high amplitude. One would thus expect that cavitation would take place in a liquid irradiated with high energy ultrasonics.

Consider a small region in a liquid through which sound waves are travelling. During the negative half of the pressure cycle the liquid is subjected to a tensile stress and during the positive half-cycle it experiences a compression. Any bubbles which are present in the liquid will thus expand and contract alternately. Where the pressure amplitude is sufficiently high and the initial radius of the bubble is less than a critical value, R_0, as given by the expression:

$$\omega^2 R_0{}^2 = 3\gamma(P_0 + 2T_s/R_0)/\rho \qquad (8.1)$$

the bubble collapses suddenly during the compression. In this equation, ω represents the angular frequency, P_0 the hydrostatic pressure in the liquid, γ the ratio of the principal specific heats of the gas contained in the bubble, and T_s the surface tension at the surface of the bubble. This sudden collapse is known as cavitation and it can result in the release of a comparatively large amount of energy almost instantaneously. The magnitude of the energy released in this way depends on the value of the ratio R_m/R_0, where R_m represents the radius of the bubble when it has expanded to its maximum size.

This ratio depends on the value of the acoustic pressure amplitude and, hence, the acoustic intensity.

Although the presence of bubbles facilitates its onset, cavitation can also occur in gas-free liquids when the acoustic pressure amplitude exceeds the hydrostatic pressure in the liquid. For part of the negative half of the pressure cycle the liquid is in a state of tension. Where this occurs, the forces of cohesion between neighbouring molecules are opposed and voids are formed at weak points in the structure of the liquid. These voids grow in size and then collapse in the same way as gas-filled bubbles. Cavities produced in this way

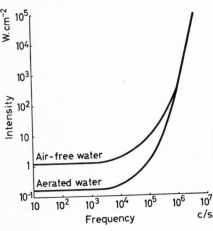

Figure 8.1. Variation of threshold intensity with frequency for water at room temperature (after Esche[2])

contain only the vapour of the liquid. Cavitation in a gas-free liquid may be induced by introducing defects in its lattice structure such as by adding impurities or by bombarding the liquid with neutrons.

The onset of cavitation is often indicated by a hissing sound called *cavitation noise*. The minimum intensity or amplitude required to produce cavitation is called the *threshold of cavitation*. This quantity and also the amount of energy released may be determined from the loss of weight due to the erosion of a solid sample placed in the liquid.

Figure 8.1 shows how the threshold intensity varies with frequency for both aerated and gas-free water. As one might expect, the threshold intensity is considerably greater for gas-free water than for aerated water. It is seen that this quantity remains constant as for frequencies up to about 10 kc/s; there is then a steady increase as the frequency is raised to about 50 kc/s and finally a rapid increase as the frequency is raised still further.

As a general rule, there is an increase in threshold intensity with rising pressure and a decrease with rising temperature. There are, however, a number of exceptions to this rule (see, for example, Hueter and Bolt[2], p. 234). The threshold intensity decreases as the time of exposure to sound is increased. This is because of a time delay between the acoustic excitation and the onset of cavitation. Thus, for pulsed waves, the threshold intensity is reduced in value as the pulse length is increased, until an upper limit is reached, after which it remains independent of pulse length. This upper limit is dependent upon frequency and would be of the order of 20 m sec for a frequency of 20 kc/s.

The quantity of energy released by cavitation is dependent upon the kinetics of the growth and collapse of the bubbles. This should increase with the surface tension at the bubble interface and decrease with the vapour pressure of the liquid. Water, because of its comparatively high surface tension is a very effective medium for cavitation. It can be made still more effective by the addition of about 10 per cent alcohol, which results in a considerable increase in vapour pressure but a decrease in surface tension. However, the added effect due to the rise in vapour pressure more than compensates for any losses due to the fall in surface tension.

Cavitation may be accompanied by a weak emission of light; this phenomenon is known as *sonoluminescence*, for which continuous spectra have been observed. There is some doubt as to the origin of this phenomenon, and the various theories put forward have been discussed by Jarman[3]. He suggested that the most likely explanation is that micro-shocks are produced in the cavities during their final collapse. As a result of these shocks the vapour becomes incandescent and there is a temperature rise of several thousand degrees. He also proposed that chemical reactions caused by cavitation might be responsible for some part of the observed sonoluminescence.

The various effects of cavitation and their applications are discussed in some of the following sections of this chapter. For optimum conditions a low frequency is chosen but there is a lower frequency limit at about 20 kc/s set by considerations of the health and comfort of the operators, who would experience unpleasant and harmful effects at frequencies below this. The method of coupling the sound energy to the region of cavitation requires careful consideration because of the necessity of avoiding cavitation in the intervening medium, where the bubbles would scatter the sound waves, thus giving rise to attenuation. This can be done with the use of a focussing system (see Section 2.14) which ensures that the threshold intensity level is exceeded only in the region where cavitation is required. Alternatively the threshold level of the coupling fluid can be suitably increased by maintaining it at an increased pressure.

Further information on the subject of cavitation may be obtained from Crawford[1] (p. 26), Hueter and Bolt[2] (p. 225), and Noltingk and Terry[4].

8.3. EMULSIFICATION AND THE PRODUCTION OF AEROSOLS

An important application of cavitation is the emulsification of a system consisting of two immiscible liquids, such as oil and water.

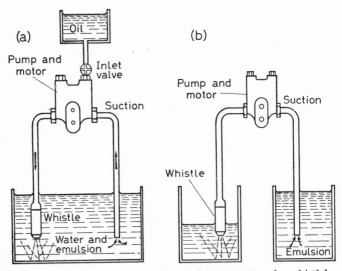

Figure 8.2. Production of emulsions using resonant wedge whistle[1]: (a) initial stage; (b) final stage

Where cavitation appears at the interface between the two liquids, very fine drops of one liquid are forced with high energies into the body of the other. Thus if a quantity of one such liquid is introduced into another through which high amplitude sound waves are passing, the added liquid rapidly breaks up into minute particles which remain suspended in the irradiated liquid, so that a highly stable emulsion is produced.

Ultrasonics are used extensively in the food, paint and polish, cosmetic, and pharmaceutical industries for the production of emulsions. *Figure 8.2* illustrates a method of preparing an oil-water emulsion with a resonant wedge whistle. First an emulsion is formed as the oil is introduced into the water (see *Figure 8.2a*) and then the mixture is refined by circulation. Finally the oil supply is disconnected and the emulsion is forced through the whistle into the second container. By this method suspensions having a mean diameter of about 2μ are obtained.

Where the two liquids have widely differing densities, such as for water and mercury, it is possible to form an emulsion by agitation alone. This kind of emulsion, however, is not very stable and the liquids separate in a very short time.

As early as 1927, Wood and Loomis showed that when a beam of intense ultrasonic waves from a transducer immersed in a liquid is directed towards the surface, a jet is thrown up from the surface and

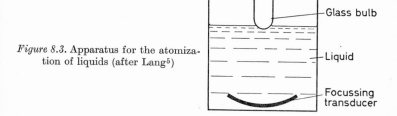

Figure 8.3. Apparatus for the atomization of liquids (after Lang[5])

a fine mist appears. The density of this mist depends on the wave intensity, and the size of the droplets depends on the frequency of the waves and the surface tension of the liquid. Lang[5] produced overwhelming evidence to show that this phenomenon is related to the production of capillary waves at the surface. He was able to generate aerosols by using frequencies ranging from 10 to 800 kc/s; *Figure 8.3* illustrates the apparatus used for the frequency range 400 to 800 kc/s. The ultrasonic beam from a curved ceramic transducer was focussed on to the base of a glass bulb placed on the liquid surface and a fine fog appeared in the vicinity of the bulb. This was accompanied by the appearance of capillary waves at the surface. With molten wax as the liquid the surface wavelength, $\lambda_{,s}$ and the particle diameter, D, were measured. It was found that the ratio D/λ_s was equal to 0·34. Lang concluded that since D was not very much less than $\lambda_s/2$ the droplets were formed by the ejection of the surface wave peaks.

The wavelength of the capillary waves was found to be given by the expression:

$$\lambda_s = 8\pi T_s/\rho f^2$$

Where T_s represents surface tension, ρ the density of the liquid, and f the frequency. Thus the particle size for a given liquid could be accurately controlled by varying the frequency.

8.4. THE EFFECTS OF ULTRASONIC WAVES ON SUSPENDED PARTICLES AND BUBBLES IN FLUIDS

When particles are suspended in a fluid irradiated with progressive ultrasonic waves, the pressure of radiation (see Section 2.9) sets the particles in motion in a direction away from the source. The mobilities of the particles depend on their sizes and on the viscosity of the fluid, as well as the acoustic intensity. In a stationary wave system, as observed in a Kundt's tube, the particles are directed away from the pressure antinodes and collect together at the pressure nodes, i.e. the displacement antinodes. This has been observed for gas bubbles occurring in stationary waves in a liquid. The bubbles collect at the pressure nodes, coalesce, and, when sufficiently large, rise to the surface. Applications of this phenomenon include the degassing of molten glass, molten metals, liquid foodstuffs prior to vacuum packing, and beer subsequent to bottling.

Ultrasonics can also be used to coagulate suspended particles in a fluid. Supposing that two particles are positioned in such a way that the line joining them is perpendicular to the direction of wave propagation. From a consideration of Bernoulli's theorem (see, for example, Newman and Searle[6], p. 363) it can be seen that the effect of the alternating fluid velocity between them is to produce a drop in pressure. The particles are then attracted to one another and coalesce. When the coagulated particles are sufficiently large they settle down under the influence of gravity. This effect is used for the dispersion of fog and smoke.

Where, however, the intensity of the sound waves in a liquid is sufficiently high, the suspended particles are broken up by cavitation and an emulsion is then formed.

8.5. ULTRASONIC CLEANING

For ultrasonic cleaning both cavitation and the agitation of the waves may be involved. At low frequencies cavitation is the principal agent but at higher frequencies the process is due entirely to agitation (cf. *Figure 8.1*).

Most cleaning applications are carried out in the frequency range

20 to 40 kc/s, where cavitation effects are most pronounced, using either ceramic or magnetostrictive sources. The work is immersed in a tank containing a liquid which is selected not only for optimum cavitation conditions but also for its cleaning characteristics, i.e. detergent properties, ability to degrease, etc. Trichlorethylene and cyclohexane have proved satisfactory in this respect. *Figure 8.4*

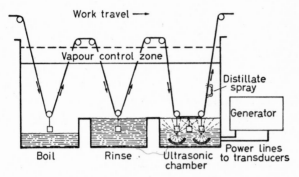

Figure 8.4. Conveyor belt arrangement for ultrasonic cleaning[1] (*diagram by courtesy of Dextrex Corporation, U.S.A.*)

illustrates a method for cleaning a large number of components which are fed to the tank by a conveyor belt.

Ultrasonic cleaning is especially useful where normal methods are either ineffective or liable to cause damage. Applications include the removal, without scratching, of lapping paste from lenses after grinding, the cleaning of grease and swarf from small orifices in engine components, and the removal of blood, etc., from surgical instruments after use. Where it is required to clean very delicate objects which might be damaged by cavitation, higher frequencies, usually from 100 kc/s to 1 Mc/s, are employed.

Attempts have been made to use ultrasonics for the laundering of clothes but they have not proved very satisfactory. More promise, however, is shown for the application of ultrasonics to the removal of localized stains from garments subjected to 'dry-cleaning'.

8.6. APPLICATIONS TO SOLIDS

When high-amplitude ultrasonic vibrations are applied to a solid specimen, it is being strained beyond its elastic limit. Consequently it may suffer a plastic deformation which increases with each cycle and eventually, provided that the amplitude is sufficiently high, breakage occurs. One such application is fatigue testing and *Figure 8.5* illustrates an arrangement designed for this purpose.

The ultrasonic drill is an application which has been developed to a considerable extent in recent years. The drilling action is reciprocal, like that of the pneumatic road drill, and holes of any desired shape may be cut in materials. One type of drill (see *Figure 3.12a*) consists of a tapered rod firmly attached at the broader end to a magneto-strictive transducer; a cutting tool is screwed to the other end. The rod, which is of resonant length, acts as a velocity transformer. The tool need only be made of a soft material, such as mild steel, because the actual cutting is performed by an abrasive slurry, such as boron carbide, silicon carbide, or aluminium oxide suspensions. The slurry is placed over the work and continually renewed during the cutting process. This method has been found highly advantageous for drilling hard and brittle materials such as glass, ceramics, tungsten carbide and germanium.

To transducer

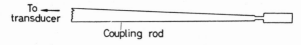

Coupling rod

Figure 8.5. Application to fatigue testing

Experiments have been conducted with the ultrasonic drill in the field of dentistry, on account of the ease with which it cuts teeth and of the action being painless. It has, however, certain disadvantages in that a continuous supply of slurry is required and that a great deal of heat is generated. Furthermore, the cutting action for soft material such as decay is not satisfactory. It is understood that the use of this drill in the United Kingdom is not, at the time of writing, approved by the British Dental Association.

8.7. METALLURGICAL APPLICATIONS

Much success has been encountered with the applications of high-energy ultrasonics to the treatment and working of metals. Apart from drilling, these include the treatment of melts, soldering and welding.

When a molten metal is cooled it is essential that all bubbles are removed before the solid state is reached, otherwise defects will occur. One way of doing this is to irradiate the melt with ultrasonic waves (see Section 8.4). If cooling occurs under normal conditions crystals begin to form at the temperature of solidification. These crystals grow to sizes which are dependent upon the rate of cooling and the types of impurity in the metal. The effect of high energy is to cause the crystals to be broken up by the action of cavitation. The solid which is finally formed has then a much finer grain structure than if cooling were to take place with the melt undisturbed.

The soldering of metals by ultrasonics can be effected without the use of any flux, so that any trouble arising from the introduction of corrosive substances is eliminated. An ultrasonic soldering iron somewhat similar in design to the ultrasonic drill is illustrated in *Figure 8.6*. The essential difference between the two instruments is

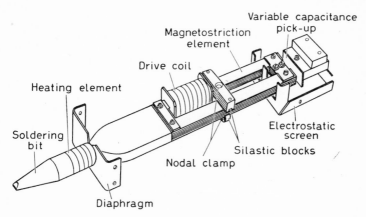

Figure 8.6. Ultrasonic soldering iron (*courtesy of Mullard, London*)

the electrically heated bit on the soldering iron which replaces the tool at the end of the ultrasonic drill. The vibrations of the bit produce cavitation in the solder, thus cleaning the surface of the work and removing any oxide coatings. An excellent adhesion of the solder to the metal surface occurs in this way.

Until the recent development of fluxes suitable for use with aluminium, ultrasonics provided the only really effective way of soldering this metal. The ultrasonic soldering iron has now been shown to be highly effective for 'micro-joints'. Hamilton[7] has reported that soldered joints have been made with 0·002-inch diameter gold wire on gold-plated silicon and also on aluminium foil only 0·003 inch thick.

One development of high-energy ultrasonics which has only just emerged from its experimental stage is that of welding. This can be done at normal temperatures without any special surface preparation and there is a further advantage in that practically no deformation occurs. The physical mechanisms involved in this process are not yet fully understood but it is probable that molecular diffusion takes place across the surfaces in contact with one another. It was at first suggested that ultrasonic welding would have a wide range of

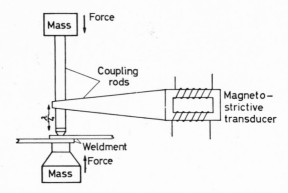

Figure 8.7. Ultrasonic welding method of Jones and Powers[8]

application but, up to now, success has been limited to the joining together of thin sheets and foils. *Figure 8.7* shows an arrangement similar to that used by Jones and Powers[8] in which a magneto-strictive oscillator working at a frequency of 25 kc/s is used. Devices of this kind have proved useful for spot-welding.

8.8. CHEMICAL EFFECTS

Ultrasonically induced cavitation in certain liquids has the effect of promoting chemical reactions within them. This may be due to electrolytic action brought about by the appearance of equal and opposite free electric charges at opposite ends of the bubbles. Other possible causes of chemical effects are the instantaneous and enormous increases in pressure, up to thousands of atmospheres, and temperature up to hundreds of degrees, in the vicinities of the cavities upon their collapse. Chemical changes are believed also to be brought about as a result of the energy released from resonant bubbles.

Where cavitation occurs in water the resultant electrolytic action separates the H_2O molecules into H and OH ions,

i.e. $$H_2O \rightarrow H + OH$$

This may be followed, according to Lindström and Lamm[9], by one or more of the following reactions:

$$H + OH \rightarrow H_2O$$
$$H + H \rightarrow H_2$$
$$H_2 + OH \rightarrow H_2O + H$$
$$OH + OH \rightarrow H_2O_2$$
$$H + H_2O_2 \rightarrow H_2O + OH$$

When certain substances are dissolved in cavitating water, oxidation or reduction may result. Oxidation may occur because of the release of hydrogen peroxide (H_2O_2), which readily provides oxygen for such a reaction, and reduction as a result of the release of hydrogen ions. For example, when potassium iodide (KI) crystals are dissolved in the water, the K and I ions are separated by electrolysis, the K ions are oxidized, and free iodine is produced.

The amount of energy released by cavitation may be sufficient to depolymerize a high polymer substance, i.e. the molecules are broken down to form smaller ones. This action has been observed with materials such as starch, gelatin, polystyrene, nitrocellulose and rubber.

Because of the very slow rates of reaction, the chemical changes induced by ultrasonics have little practical application. However, it has been found that cavitation has proved to be a valuable tool for accelerating chemical changes, which include not only those mentioned above but also polymerization and molecular rearrangement. One application which has met with success is the decrease in the maturing time of wines and spirits from several months to only a week or so.

Fuller accounts of the chemical effects of high-energy ultrasonics have been given by Crawford[1] and Weissler[10].

8.9. BIOLOGICAL EFFECTS AND MEDICAL APPLICATIONS

The effects of high energy ultrasonics on living matter include the disruption of cells by cavitation, the damage of body tissue by agitation, and the heating of bone and muscle. Airborne ultrasonics of sufficiently high power, having frequencies of up to 30 kc/s, have been shown to cause unpleasant and sometimes harmful effects on both human beings and animals. For example, persons operating high-power ultrasonic equipment for long periods are subjected to fatigue and sometimes nausea. On the other hand, high-energy ultrasonics have proved successful in scaring away birds.

Much research has been done on the destruction of malignant tissue by ultrasonics but there are conflicting reports as to whether or not this method is sufficiently selective for effective use. The heating effect of ultrasonics, however, appears to show the most promise in medicine at present, and there are wide applications of this in the U.S.A. and Germany to the treatment of such muscular ailments as lumbago. Because of the necessity of focussing the waves into selected zones, frequencies as high as one or two megacycles are often used. Some work has also been done on the application of ultrasonic heating to the temporary blocking of nerves with a view to analgesia. The margin of safety, however, between the reversible and irreversible blocking is too narrow for the method to be brought into practice at present.

Ultrasonics have been used successfully to kill bacteria suspended in liquids, one application being the sterilization of milk. Another biological effect of ultrasonics which has been applied in the food industry is the tenderizing of meat by the action of breaking down its fibres.

REFERENCES

1. CRAWFORD, A. E. *Ultrasonic Engineering,* Butterworths, London, 1955
2. HUETER, T. F. and BOLT, R. H. *Sonics,* Wiley, New York/Chapman and Hall, London, 1955
3. JARMAN, P. *J. acoust. Soc. Amer.,* 1960, **32,** 1459
4. NOLTINGK, B. E. and TERRY, N. B. *Technical Aspects of Sound* (ed. E. G. Richardson), Vol. 2, Elsevier, Amsterdam, 1957, p. 154
5. LANG, R. J. *J. acoust. Soc. Amer.,* 1962, **34,** 6
6. NEWMAN, F. H. and SEARLE, V. H. L. *The General Properties of Matter,* 5th Edn., Arnold, London, 1957
7. HAMILTON, R. *Using Ultrasonics,* issued free by the Information Division, D.S.I.R., State House, High Holborn, London, W.C.1 (no date)
8. JONES, J. B. and POWERS, J. J. *Welding J.,* 1956, **35,** 761
9. LINDSTRÖM, O. and LAMM, O. *J. phys. and colloid. Chem.,* 1951, **55,** 1138
10. WEISSLER, A. *J. acoust. Soc. Amer.,* 1953, **25,** 651

INDEX

Italic figures denote references extending to subsequent pages

Absorption coefficient, *17*
Absorption
  gases, *88*
  hysteretic type, *18*
  liquids, *118*
  solids, *149*
  relaxational type, *19*
Acoustoelectric effect, *169*
Aerosols, coagulation of, 204
Aerosols, production of, *203*
Airborne applications, *194*
Ammonium dihydrogen phosphate
  (ADP), 49, *56*
Amplification, ultrasonic waves,
  171
Anisotropy, solids, 149, 151, 152
Atomization of liquids, *203*
Attenuation, plane waves, *17*
Attenuation, solids, *149*
  (*see also* Absorption)

Bardeen-Cooper-Schrieffer (BCS)
  theory, 164
Barium titanate, 45, 49, 57
Biological effects, *209*
Blind persons, guidance of, 195

Cadmium sulphide, 85, *171*
Calorimeters, acoustic, *82*
Cavitation, *199*
Cavity resonators, *71*
Chemical detectors, *83*
Chemical effects, 105, *208*
Cleaning, *204*
Coagulation, 204
Compression waves, (*see* Longitu-
  dinal waves)
Coupling, transducer, 58, 70, *173*
Critical state, *124*
Crystal mounting, *57*, 58, 113, *114*,
  133, *173*, 176, 186

Crystal oscillators, *41*
Crystal receivers, *60*
Crystal sources, preparation of, *57*
Curie temperature, 45
Cyclotron effect, *164*

Damping capacity, 18, *179*
Delay lines, *189*
Depletion layer transducers, 85
Diffraction, 30, *35*, 110
Diffraction grating, ultrasonic, 84,
  193
Dislocations, *154*
Dispersion of particles, 204
Doppler effect, *38*, *195*, 197
Drill, ultrasonic, 70, 206
ΔE effect, *158*

Electrokinetic microphone, 84
Electromagnetic transducers, *79*
Electro-mechanical coupling, 50
Electron-phonon interactions, *160*
Electrostatic transducers, *80*
Electrostrictive effect, *44*, *157*
Emulsification, *202*
Energy density, *15*
Energy, vibrations, *7*
Equivalent circuits, transducers,
  21

Fatigue testing, 206
Ferrites, 63, 66, 68
Ferroelectric materials, absorption
  in, *157*
Ferromagnetic materials, absorp-
  tion in, *157*
Flaw detection, *185*
Flowmeter, *195*
Focussing systems, *37*
Freedom, degrees of, *93*
Frequency response curves, 9

211

Gallium arsenide, 85
Galton whistle, 72
Gases, measurements in, *105*
Grain boundary losses, *151*

Hartmann generator, *72*
Helium, liquid, *131*
Hot-wire microphone, *81*
Hypersonic waves, liquids, 145
  solids, *167, 181*
Hysteretic losses, *156, 158*

Image converters, 192
Immersion technique, 186
Impedance
  characteristic, 14, 26
  matching, 55
  mechanical, 8
  methods, *141*, 181
  specific acoustic, *13*
Impurities in gases, 111
  (*see also* Mixtures, gases)
Impurity atoms, *153*
Intensity, *15*
Interferometer, acoustic, *33, 106, 135*, 179
  fixed path, 113
Internal friction (*see* Absorption)
Interstitial atoms, *153*
Isomeric relaxation, *119*

Lamb waves, 188
Lattice imperfections, *153*
Lead zirconate, 45, 49, 57
Level indicator, 198
Liquid helium, *131*
Liquids, electrically conducting, 58, 134
Liquids, measurements in, *117*
Love waves, 148

Magnetic field, effect on attenuation, *159, 164*
Magneto-acoustic effect, *159, 164*
Magnetostrictive effect, *62, 157*
Magnetostrictive generators, *68*
Magnetostrictive materials, *67,157*
  properties of, *65*

Magnetostrictive oscillators, *62*
Magnetostrictive, receivers, *70*
Matching, transducer, 55
  (*see also* Coupling, transducer)
Measurements, gases, *105*
Measurements, liquids, *133*
Measurements, solids, *173*
Mechanical, generators, *71*
Mechanical receivers, *76*
Medical applications, *196, 209*
Metallurgical applications, *206*
Micro-eddy currents, 159
Microwave ultrasonics (*see* Hypersonic waves)
Mixtures, gases, *103*
  (*see also* Impurities in gases)
Mixtures, liquids, *123*
Mode conversion, *28, 37, 187*
Mosaic transducers, 59
Moving coil transducer, 79
Moving iron transducer, 78, 79

Nuclear magnetic resonance, *170*

Optical detectors, 84
Optical diffraction method, *138*
Optical methods, liquids, 137
Optical methods, solids, 181

Phonon, 133, 160
Phonon-phonon interactions, *168*
Photosensitive attenuation, *171*
Pierce circuit, 43, 64
Piezoelectric crystals, properties of, 49, *55*
Piezoelectric effect, *41*
Piezoelectric oscillators, *41*
Piezoelectric receivers, *60*
Piezoelectric relations, *45*
Piezoelectric semiconductors, 85
Polycrystalline solids, 148, *150*
Pressure of radiation, *16*
Pressure measurements, 196
Probes
  angled, 187
  longitudinal wave, 186
  shear wave, *187*

Progressive wave measurements, *134*, 180

Pulse technique, *136, 174, 185*

'Q' factor, 9
'Q' of transducer, *54*
Quartz crystals, *41*, 49, 56
Quartz, elastic constants of, 48

Radiometers, *77*
Rayleigh cross-modes, 37
Rayleigh disc, *76*
Rayleigh waves, 149
Reflection coefficient, 25
Reflection, plane waves, *24*
Refraction, plane waves, *28*
Relaxation frequency, 23
Relaxation, general theory of, *22*
Relaxation time, 22
  (*see also* Absorption)
  variation with pressure, 99
  variation with temperature, 99, 123, 154
Resonance, *9*, 22
Reverberation method, *140*, 181
Rochelle salt, 49, 57
Roton, 133

Sandwich transducers, *59*
Scattering in solids, *152*
'Sing around' method, 179
Siren, ultrasonic, *75*
Soldering, ultrasonic, 207
Solids, measurements in, *173*
Sonoluminescence, 201
Stationary wave methods, *179*
  (*see also* Interferometer, acoustic)
Stress measurement, *191*
Striation method, *137*
Stroboscope, ultrasonic, 194
Structural relaxation, *120*, 170
Substitutional atoms, 153
Superconductivity, *160, 163*
Suspended particles, coagulation of, 204
Suspended particle method, 76

Thermal conduction, 21, *90*, 118, 167
Thermal effects, single crystals, *167*
Thermal relaxation, *93, 95, 119*, 170
Thermal transducers, *81*
Thermocouple transducer, 82
Thermoelastic relaxation, *150*
Thickness gauging, 189
Total reflection method, 181
Transducer theory, *45, 50, 61, 64, 66*
Transducers
  barium titanate, 45, 49, 57
  cadmium sulphide, 85
  chemical, *83*
  coupling, 58, 70, *173*
  depletion layer, 85
  electromagnetic, *79*
  electrostatic, *80*
  equivalent circuits of, *51*
  ferrite, 63, 66, 68
  gallium arsenide, 85
  lead zirconate, 45, 49, 57
  magnetostrictive, 62
  matching, 55
  mechanical, *71*
  mosaic, 59
  moving coil, 79
  moving iron, 78, 79
  optical, *84*
  piezoelectric, *41*, 85
  'Q' of, *54*
  quartz, *41*, 49, 56
  Rochelle salt, 49, 57
  sandwich, *59*
  thermal, *81*
  (*see also* Crystal oscillators, Probes, etc.)
Transformation factor, *50*, 67
Transmission coefficient, 25
Transmission, plane waves, *24*

UHF waves (*see* Hypersonic waves)
Underwater applications, 194

Velocity dispersion, 23, *88*, *93*, *118*, *121*
  (*see also* Absorption)
Velocity
  gases, *87*
  of light, measurement, 194
  liquid mixtures, *123*
  liquids, *117*
  plane waves, *11*
  solids, *147*
Vibrations
  energy of, 7
  forced, *8*
  free, *6*
Viscometer, ultrasonic, 195
Viscoelastic liquids, 127, *130*
Viscosity, *88*, 117, 118, *127*
Viscous waves, *127*
Vortex whistle, *74*

Wave equation, 10

Wave guides, acoustic, 37
Wave vectors, 10
  relations between, 14
Waves
  compression, 5
  Lamb, 188
  longitudinal, 5
    solids, *147*
  Rayleigh, 149
  shear, 5
    applications, 187
    liquids, *127*
      measurements, 143
    polarization, *191*
    solids, 29, 148
  stationary (or standing), *31*
  surface, 30, *148*, *187*
  transverse, 5
Wedge resonator, 74
Welding, ultrasonic, *207*
Whistles, ultrasonic, *71*